The Reproduction of Life

THE
REPRODUCTION
OF
LIFE

ROBERT L. LEHRMAN

Illustrated by the author

Basic Books, Inc., Publishers
NEW YORK
LONDON

Preface

Through the ages, no phenomenon has stirred man's imagination and curiosity more than the growth and reproduction of living things. Every people has its creation myths, its attempts to understand the facts of life around it by unifying all that it sees under a common set of principles. Many of the spirits and gods of primitive peoples are the result of this attempt to explain the succession of generations, forever begetting new generations, always according to kind.

With the coming of scientific biology, unifying principles were sought in the phenomena themselves, and many were found. Growth and reproduction, repair of injuries and regeneration of lost parts, all were seen to depend on common underlying phenomena. But the essence of these phenomena have, until very recently, remained as mysterious as the spirits of the cave men. Today, the dark curtain is lifting. With new information in biochemistry, aided by radioactive materials and the electron microscope, we are reaching into the most intimate structure of living things and bringing to the light of understanding the mystery that has puzzled mankind for so long. The events of the past few years have ushered in a new era of biological understanding, the greatest since Charles Darwin propounded the theory that evolution is a law of life.

The purpose of this book is to tell the layman the story of our knowledge of the reproduction of life. We will investigate the process of reproduction not only in its obvious macroscopic forms, but also in the events that can be seen

» » *v*

only with a microscope and in those that occur on too small a scale to be seen at all. We will find underlying unities that were only guessed at ten years ago.

This book covers such a wide range of topics in biological science that it would be difficult for one individual to guarantee the accuracy of all its parts. Accordingly, several distinguished biologists have read various parts of the book for accuracy, and I would like to express my thanks to Dr. Lilo Grothe, Dr. Marjory J. Nelson, Dr. Daniel S. Lehrman, Mr. James Klausen, Dr. Joseph J. Copeland, Dr. Robert W. Merriam, and Mrs. Edith Wallace for reading and commenting on the manuscript. I have not, however, always followed their advice, and any remaining errors, as well as all opinions and speculations, are mine alone.

January 1964   R. L. L.

Contents

Illustrations

The Reproduction of Life

1

*The Continuity
of Life*

To a man of the sixteenth century, the world was full of hidden corners where vermin of all sorts arose from decaying refuse. In his daily life he was in intimate contact with garbage and sewage, rotten and insect-ridden food, rats and mice, maggots, lice, and fleas. When he saw beetles crawling in manure, he never questioned that the beetles were a direct result of the decay of manure. And who could doubt that a piece of meat, if not eaten soon, would turn into maggots? When a famous naturalist wrote that he had found a formula for making mice, no one saw reason to doubt it. He simply incubated wheat germ in a dirty shirt for twenty-one days; it apparently never occurred to him to keep mice out.

The concept of "spontaneous generation"—that life arises spontaneously from offal—was accepted on the best of authority, for it was based on the natural philosophy of Aristotle himself. Three hundred years before the Christian

Era, the first great biologist had worked out a comprehensive classification of living things, had studied their anatomy, and had produced an over-all biological theory. The keystone of his theory was the idea that what distinguishes living matter from nonliving matter is a mysterious inner essence—a soul. This inner essence, he said, is transmitted to nonliving matter when a living creature grows and reproduces by assimilating the nonliving substance it uses as food. This concept was quite radical for Aristotle's time. It took a man of great understanding to realize, in that day, that food is converted into living matter.

Aristotle went further. The inner essence of life is also present, he said, in the earth, and to some degree in the other "elements" of ancient Greek philosophy: air, fire, and water. According to Aristotle, any of these elements could create life by bestowing this inner essence on lifeless matter. The morning dew produced worms, beetle larvae, ticks, and fireflies; decaying fruit or manure could create lice, moths, mosquitoes, and flies. Even such complex creatures as fish, crabs, mice, and frogs might be generated from soil or from various forms of slime. The spontaneous generation of living creatures from nonliving matter was just as natural, just as understandable, and just as mysterious as the birth of a baby.

LIFE FROM LIFE

One of the first experiments in biology dealt with the question of spontaneous generation. The famous controlled experiments of the Italian professor of medicine, Francisco Redi, proved conclusively that maggots can develop in meat only if flies are allowed to lay eggs in the meat. Redi's work is well known, but not many people realize that its great importance lies not in the attack on the theory of spontaneous generation, but in the adoption of a new method of acquiring knowledge.

For the first twelve or thirteen centuries of the Christian Era, very little was known about the world. The works of the ancient philosophers, particularly Aristotle, were considered the source of all knowledge. Redi was one of the pioneers of a new attitude, that new information should be sought not only in Aristotle, but also where Aristotle sought it—in nature. The scientific method was coming into its own. In the ensuing centuries, it was applied to the problem of spontaneous generation of many different organisms. A series of supposed instances of spontaneous generation were discredited as parents were discovered lurking in the background. By 1800, natural philosophers were writing of a law of *biogenesis*. This means simply that every living creature comes from living parents.

How do you prove a law like that? Actually, you do not. No amount of accumulating evidence can ever eliminate the possibility that the next case to be investigated will be an authentic specimen of spontaneous generation. But advancing knowledge makes it seem increasingly unlikely that such a process occurs. And that is what happened. Knowledge of the great complexity of structure of living things was accumulating rapidly during those years. In time, the idea that the organs within animals, the cells within organs, and even the tiny structures within the cells could be created spontaneously out of a bit of stinking meat began to seem ridiculous.

Still, this is not proof. When the early crude microscopes revealed enormous swarms of bacteria in every piece of putrid meat and rotting plant, the theory of spontaneous generation received a boost. The early-nineteenth-century mind boggled at the thought of a frog, with its complex structure, being spawned by the mud of a river bank, but bacteria were another matter altogether. These tiny specks seemed hardly more complex than the slime from which they seemed to come.

In the nineteenth century, two conflicting theories were put forward to account for these countless bacteria. One held that the law of biogenesis applied to bacteria as well as to larger organisms. According to this theory, the millions of bacteria are formed by reproduction from one or a few individual bacteria that fall in from the air, where they float as dust particles. Decay is the result of the vital processes of these growing and reproducing bacteria, which use dead organisms as food.

A great French biologist, Count Buffon, would have none of this idea. He, and many others at that time, proposed a theory known as *vitalism*. This theory held that a dead organism decays spontaneously, its substance disintegrating into the "organic molecules" of which it is composed. Each "organic molecule" possesses a "vital force," which gives it the properties of life. It is the reassembly of the molecules that produces the living particles called bacteria. Bacteria are the result, not the cause, of decay.

This sounds like the same old Aristotelian doctrine of the inner essence of life, and indeed it is similar. But there is a great difference between the spontaneous generation controversy in the nineteenth century and the same argument in the sixteenth. For the vitalists were scientists. They attempted to support their ideas by experiment, not by appeals to authority and by exegesis of the ancient philosophers. The intellectual climate of the world had changed so much in the intervening three hundred years that only a scientific answer to the ancient question could have any meaning. It was the same old fight, but now both sides agreed on the ground rules. There was even a committee of judges and a prize purse: the French Academy of Sciences offered a prize for convincing experiments that would clarify the question.

The prize was awarded to "the most perfect man ever to enter the kingdom of science," Louis Pasteur. His answer to the experiments of the vitalists was simple and direct: Gentlemen, you do not appreciate the care necessary to avoid contaminating your broth with as much as a single speck of dust. Pasteur demonstrated in many ways that a broth could be kept clear and would not decay if all dust was meticulously excluded after the broth had been sterilized.

In one of his last experiments in this area, Pasteur arranged for air to enter the flask, to counter the argument that the life force could operate only in the presence of fresh air. He put gravy into a flask, then melted the neck, and drew it out into a long S-curve. Then he boiled the gravy to kill any bacteria that might be in it, and allowed it to cool. Air could enter the flask, but dust collected in the curve. The gravy remained clear, but if a little dust from the air was added, it became turbid with countless bacteria in a few days. Some of Pasteur's flasks are still sterile today, after a hundred years of exposure to open air. And to the present day, no one has disputed Pasteur's results.

Pasteur did a great deal to bury the theory of spontaneous generation, but in the last analysis, the nineteenth century abandoned it for the same reason that it had previously been abandoned. Studies of bacteria, improved microscopes, the growth of biochemistry have shown us that even tiny bacteria are in fact highly complex. They are by no means the simple specks of protoplasm which nineteenth-century biologists visualized. Today, it is not much easier to believe in the spontaneous generation of bacteria than of frogs. Most biologists doubt that life can originate anew anywhere on earth, at least in the classic sense. In spite of certain peculiar properties of viruses and the fact that life *did* originate at least once, the biogenetic law is accepted as a sound basis for today's biology.

The knowledge that living creatures arise only from other organisms implies an idea of great significance: that life is a unity, that all living creatures are related to one another. Life must have begun at some time in the past, but whatever it was that started off the endless process of begetting can never happen again. (We will come back to this idea a little later to try to account for it.) Once life appeared, its own inner necessities inevitably led to the evolutionary process that populated the earth with its rich variety of animals and plants.

For the fundamental necessity of life, the most characteristic phenomenon that distinguishes living things from inert—Aristotle's "inner essence" and Buffon's "vital force" —is nothing more or less than the ability to reproduce. Every man and tree, each fish and bacterium owes its existence to the process of reproduction. But to understand the nature of life, we must have a much deeper understanding of the meaning of reproduction. For within your body, each cell has had its origin in another cell. Like whole organisms, cells cannot originate anew. And within cells, many parts— the nucleus, the plastids and centrosomes, and probably also the mitochondria—can only originate from other structures like themselves. If we search within the nucleus, we find the same law repeating itself at still lower levels. The chromosomes, and even some of the very molecules of which these chromosomes are made, are self-duplicating. At every level, the law of life is reproduction. The purpose of this book is to explore the process of reproduction at each of these levels and so to gain a deeper understanding of the meaning of the process we call "life."

LIVING AND NONLIVING

Discarding the theory of spontaneous generation, man has taken up the concept of the unity of all living things. Twentieth-century biology has developed this idea far beyond anything that Pasteur could have imagined. Today we know enough about evolution to have an excellent over-all picture of how ancient simple organisms have given rise to the complex and diverse inhabitants of the earth. Perhaps even more significant is the high degree of inner unity found alongside the diversity. In structure, the cells of all higher animals and plants are remarkably similar. They all consist of nucleus and cytoplasm and contain such structures as mitochondria, cell membranes, and chromosomes. The chemical similarities are even more noteworthy. Some of the processes that supply the energy of a yeast cell also help to keep giraffes and geraniums going.

But another kind of unity which has long been recognized is the unity of the living and nonliving. The earliest chemical investigation of the composition of living things revealed the existence of a category of chemicals—mostly large molecules of carbon, hydrogen, oxygen, and (often) nitrogen—which were never found outside of living things. These were called "organic" chemicals, and it was believed that they were made only in living cells, where they were produced from simpler materials by the action of the vital force. Living substance and nonliving substance were fundamentally different from each other. Living matter, by virtue of a unique kind of energy (vital force) built itself into a different kind of matter than that which makes up the rest of the universe. This theory was first attacked in 1860, when the French chemist Marcellin Berthelot published a book, based on many experiments, which showed that the same laws of chemistry apply to both organic and inorganic matter. Since then, ever-more-complex organic compounds have emerged from the test tube, and the biochemist is now well on the road to the synthesis of the fantastically complex molecules of proteins. In addition, the vague concepts of vitalism have been replaced by detailed knowledge of the chemical energetics of the life processes. What has emerged is an ever-clearer picture of living material as a chemical system of great complexity, but obeying the same laws as the rest of the universe. The peculiarly vital process, reproduction, arises from the organization of ordinary materials in a highly extraordinary way. Even the thoughts that go through your mind as you read this are produced by a special, complex arrangement of the same kinds of matter and energy of which the inert world is composed.

Since living and nonliving matter are composed of the same materials, it should not be surprising to find that there is a substance that possesses both kinds of properties. These borderline objects, sometimes alive and sometimes inert, are the *viruses*. We will have much to say about them later, for they have given biologists much of their knowledge of the chemical part of the reproductive process. What are they, and how were they found?

In the exciting early days of the germ theory of disease, the mid-nineteenth century, microscopic studies were finding in rapid succession the bacteria that cause common diseases. Anthrax, diphtheria, tuberculosis, gonorrhea, and many other diseases were shown to be invariably associated with an infestation by bacteria, each disease with its own particular kind. But certain diseases were hold-outs; no one was able to find the germ of rabies, or of smallpox, or of yellow fever. These diseases were known to be infectious, and therefore, according to the germ theory, must be caused by parasitic organisms. In the 1890's, the existence of parasites too small to be seen with the microscope was conclusively proved.

The first proof came in the studies of tobacco mosaic disease, in which the leaves of the tobacco plants become covered with brown or black circular spots which destroy the crop. If the infected leaves are macerated thoroughly in water and the mixture forced through a filter of unglazed porcelain, the filter holds back all bacteria and other particles big enough to be seen in a microscope, so that only a clear fluid passes through. If this fluid is applied to the leaves of a tobacco plant, the typical, round spots of the mosaic disease appear. Tiny amounts of the fluid can produce widespread disease, and the process can be repeated indefinitely. Whatever causes tobacco mosaic disease is obviously capable of reproduction and must, therefore, be thought of as living.

This technique soon established that foot-and-mouth disease of cattle is caused by an organism of a similar nature, and proof for other diseases, such as rabies, smallpox, measles, and polio soon followed. The organisms were at first called "filtrable viruses," but we now refer to them simply as "viruses." These viruses are nearly always pathogenic (disease-causing), and are capable of living and reproducing only within a living cell. They are known to cause many diseases of animals, plants, and man in addition to those listed above. Viruses are responsible for several forms of cancer in fowls, mice, and other animals. It was suggested many years ago that some forms of human cancer might be due to viruses, and this theory has been alternately in and out of favor with pathologists for some time; at the present writing it seems to be on the way back in. We now know that the common cold is due to an infection by any of several viruses. In 1915 two French bacteriologists, Twort and D'Herelle, found carefully cultured bacteria dying on their Petri plates. When they investigated the reasons, they found to their amazement that the bacteria were being killed by an invisible infectious organism which they called "bacteriophage" (bacteria-eater).

This infection is now recognized as a type of virus. The obvious hope that these bacterial viruses may supply a weapon for fighting bacterial disease has diminished through the years, but the bacterial viruses have been most useful in another regard: they have been the chief subject in the study of the chemical mechanisms by which viruses live and reproduce.

Heroic attempts to see viruses in the early years of virus research were rewarded with extremely meager results. No one could be really sure that the tiny specks seen in a dark field microscope, looking like dust particles dancing in a sunbeam, were really the largest of the virus particles. Until the invention of the electron microscope in 1931, virologists worked with organisms whose very existence could be inferred only from their effects. We now have excellent pictures, taken with electron microscope magnifications up to two hundred thousand times, of a variety of spheres, rods, threads, and tadpole-shaped particles which are undoubtedly the elusive viruses.

THE LIVING NONLIVING

Up to this time, viruses were thought of as simply small organisms. But in 1935, an American, Wendell M. Stanley, found a most fundamental difference between viruses and all other organisms—so basic, in fact, that it raised the question of whether viruses could be considered organisms at all! Stanley was attempting to isolate the virus of tobacco mosaic disease in pure form. He macerated infected leaves in water and filtered the mixture, separating a clear liquid from a solid part. In separate trials, the solid and the liquid were tested by putting them on tobacco leaves, and the virus was found to be in the clear liquid. Stanley then added a salt to the filtrate and obtained a precipitate, which was filtered out. Again both parts of the material were tested. This process was repeated again and again with various salts, each precipitation eliminating extraneous material and concentrating the elusive virus.

When Stanley finished, he had concentrated the infective power of the original leaves into a tiny amount of clear liquid. When this was evaporated to dryness, Stanley was left with a tiny mass of crystals—representing only 0.3 per cent of the original weight of the infected leaves—that possessed all the infective ability of the original leaves. He had isolated the pure virus in the form of crystals.

There is nothing else as inert as a crystal. In a crystal, each molecule has the same unchanging composition. The molecules are all alike, and all are fixed in position, forming some kind of nearly perfect pattern. Crystals, including virus crystals, remain unchanged indefinitely unless some external force acts on them. This condition contrasts sharply with the situation inside a living cell. Here all is change and restlessness, and nothing is ever as it was a moment before. Many molecules are unstable and will change into something else at the earliest opportunity. Structure and function are maintained only by continuous creation of new living substance, for any molecule that is now part of a cell will soon be changed into the wastes of its chemical processes. And yet it was only necessary to introduce the crystallized virus into a living tobacco leaf, and it would reproduce itself many thousandfold in a few days!

Surely this substance is on that fuzzy boundary between the living and nonliving: crystalline when isolated, but capable of reproduction when within the appropriate cytoplasm. A vague boundary has replaced the absolute distinction between the living and the nonliving.

Once viruses were available in pure form, it was possible to analyze them chemically. It was soon clear that viruses are composed of two of the kinds of giant molecules found in cellular organisms. A virus is made of the same two kinds of chemicals as a chromosome: proteins and nucleic acids. Combined chemical and electron-microscopical work has shown that the tobacco mosaic virus consists of a hollow cylinder made of about 2800 protein molecules arranged in a helix (the shape of a coil spring) which makes up ninety-four per cent of the weight of the particle. The remaining six per cent is nucleic acid, forming a long core within the cylinder.

Stanley's "crystals" take on a different meaning when we understand this structure. A crystal is an aggregate of molecules, and the virus particles contain many molecules. The crystal-like aggregates of tobacco mosaic viruses are unquestionably inert. Recently the virus of poliomyelitis, which is quite small and probably does consist of a single molecule, has been formed into true crystals. Stanley's interpretation of the nature of a virus as a molecule that can take on the minimum properties of life has been substantiated.

Stanley's work on the chemical nature of viruses is continuing under his direction at the Virus Laboratory of the University of California at Berkeley. Some recent results have almost accomplished a feat that has been a dream for hundreds of years: creating of life in a test tube! Pure tobacco mosaic virus can be separated chemically into its nucleic acid and its protein components, and the protein part into separate molecules. If a solution of the proteins is allowed to stand under appropriate conditions, the molecules spontaneously join together to form little hollow discs, which can readily be seen under the electron microscope. The discs then stack themselves together into hollow cylinders of random lengths. However, if the nucleic acid component is included in the mixture, the cylinders form around a core of nucleic acid, and the cylinders are all of uniform length. These newly reconstituted virus particles have all the physical, chemical, and biological properties of natural tobacco mosaic virus.

It seemed, when this work was reported, that a living creature had been taken apart and put back together again. But if we understand the nature of the virus particle, we must admit that this interpretation is exaggerated. When a virus particle attacks a cell, the protein coat does not enter the cell; only the nucleic acid core penetrates the living substance of the host. It is this nucleic acid core that is the living, reproducing structure. It somehow commandeers the vital mechanism of the host cell, so that the chemical systems of the host cell begin to make copies of the alien nucleic acid molecule, instead of contributing to the growth of the cell itself. When many such copies have been made, each makes further use of the chemical systems of the host cell and produces its protein coat. All this is destructive to the host cell, which dies. The full virus particles are then liberated, ready to squirt their nucleic acid cores into other cells. The protein coat is characteristic of the virus during its inert, crystallizable phase. The vital, reproducing part is the nucleic acid core, which has all the biological activity of the whole particle. The protein coat serves only to transport the nucleic acid core from one cell to another.

It seems, then, that reassembling a dissociated virus particle does not really qualify as a process of creating life. The problem of synthesizing living substance in its simplest form now seems to resolve itself into the chemical synthesis of a single molecule of nucleic acid!

Nonliving into Living

We accept the law of biogenesis today as a fundamental biological rule, but as we have seen, we must not make the mistake of interpreting it to mean that there is an absolute and impenetrable barrier between the living and the nonliving. If we stop to think about it, we must realize that the conversion of nonliving substance into living is as ubiquitous as life itself.

To make this point clear, let us, in imagination, repeat the famous experiment of Francisco Redi, but with some modifications. As he did, we will put some meat in a jar and allow flies to lay eggs on it. We will then seal the jar and observe the development of maggots. We will be sure to make the jar quite large so that there will be sufficient oxygen to support the maggots. In our experiment, we will weigh the jar just after we seal it and then again when the maggots are full grown. Since the jar has been sealed, nothing has been permitted to enter or leave the jar while the maggots were developing. At the end of the experiment, we would find that the jar weighs exactly the same as it did at the beginning.

Now what has happened to the quantity of living matter in the jar? Each tiny egg has developed into a fat white maggot, thousands of times the size of the original egg. The weight of living matter has increased several thousandfold. The meat has decreased in weight even more than the living matter has increased, since part of the meat has been changed into waste products of the growing maggots. But a large part of the missing meat has also been changed into the living substance of the maggots.

Was Buffon right after all? Does living matter arise from dead? Most certainly it does, but not in the sense that Buffon had in mind. For he believed that this transformation could occur *spontaneously,* whereas in our experiment, we had to put some living substance—flies' eggs—into the jar to make the meat come to life in the form of maggots. Dead matter does become living matter, but only as a result of being processed by something already alive. The maggots *assimilate* the meat, converting the dead substance of the meat into the living substance of their own bodies.

Any reproductive process involves an increase in the total quantity of living matter in the world. A mouse bears six young, each formed by the repeated division of a single cell, a fertilized egg. But each cell had to grow to full size before it could divide again. Its growth is accomplished by a process of converting food materials taken in by the cell into the living substance of the cell itself. All reproductive processes must be built on the base of this assimilation process. And assimilation is itself a kind of reproduction, a chemical reproduction, for it consists of a cell's duplicating the molecules of which it itself is composed. Assimilation began when life began, and by virtue of this process, living creatures have occupied the earth.

2

The Origin
of Life

How did it all start? Life is a flame that was kindled on earth only once and, having been kindled, became a conflagration. Five billion years ago, no green thing covered the rocks of the mountains or the lifeless soil of the valleys; nothing swam through the sterile waters of the rivers and oceans. Then, somehow, living creatures appeared on earth. Assimilating and reproducing, they eventually conquered nearly every corner of the earth, from the desert to the jungle and from the high mountains to the depths of the sea. If life cannot now originate anew, how did it start in the first place, and why can it not start again?

Many men have tried to answer these questions, and it may seem that there is no possible way to investigate something that happened billions of years ago and can happen no more. Until 1936, all discussions of the origin of life on earth were highly speculative, but in that year a Russian physiologist named A. I. Oparin put the question on a scientific basis with the publication of a well-documented theory. Gathering data from many fields of science and carefully evaluating ideas put forth by others, he presented an evolutionary picture of the origin of life, giving evidence for a step-by-step process that took many millions of years and culminated in the first organisms. Many details of his hypothesis are still in doubt, and some are unquestionably wrong, but no biologist today doubts that Oparin's broad outlines of the process that led to life on earth are correct.

Long before Oparin, it was clear that the organisms that live in the world today have developed as the result of evolution. The reproduction process is imperfect in the sense that offspring are never exactly like their parents. These differences, under appropriate conditions, accumulate for millions of years, until after many generations living things may bear little resemblance to their ancestors. In favorable circumstances, one species evolves into several others, so that the number of kinds tends to increase despite the fact that many kinds become extinct. Life was confined at first to the ocean, and the living things of that period were much simpler than those today. Complexity increases over the years. For example, single cells may form colonies, which can evolve into many-celled organisms. All our knowledge about evolution points to the fact that the earliest living creatures were single-celled ocean dwellers. Oparin projected the evolutionary process back beyond these primordial cells to the earth itself.

OPARIN'S THEORY

Oparin began with a consideration of the earth as it is believed to have been at an early stage: a mass of inert rock overlaid by a hot ocean and atmosphere, both consisting mainly of water, ammonia, and hydrogen sulfide. Since the chemistry of life is the chemistry of carbon compounds, it is important to know in what form the earth's carbon existed at that time. Apparently it was present in the form of carbides—compounds of carbon with iron and other metals—deep inside the crust. These carbides reacted with the water trapped in the crystals of the deep rocks to form simple hydrocarbons, compounds of hydrogen and carbon. These hydrocarbons were released into the atmosphere, possibly by volcanic activity, until large amounts of methane, ethane, and propane were added to the original materials of the atmosphere and ocean.

There were, then, organic chemicals in the atmosphere. But these small, simple molecules are a far cry from the giant proteins and other molecules in living cells. Oparin suggested that lightning and ultraviolet light from the sun could supply the energy to combine simple molecules into larger ones. Since there was no oxygen in the atmosphere to block the ultraviolet light, there must have been a great deal more of it then than there is now. Recent experiments have fully justified this idea, for electrical discharges and ultraviolet light passed through a mixture of hydrocarbons, ammonia, and water vapor have yielded many organic compounds, including amino acids, which are the building blocks of proteins. A recent experiment shows that this synthesis can also be produced by waves of high pressure passing through the water, such as might have been generated by meteors falling into the sea. As the organic molecules grew larger and more complex by this process, they accumulated in the ocean in large quantities. The ocean became a "thin, hot soup," an enormous reaction vessel in which the next stages of chemical building could occur. The complex molecules of carbon, hydrogen, oxygen, and nitrogen that make up the simpler organic chemicals were ready for the next step.

This next step in the evolutionary process was *polymerization*, which is the joining together of small molecules to form large ones. Organic compounds are capable of uniting together into enormous molecules, up to a million or more times as large as a water molecule. These giant molecules—the proteins, nucleic acids, fats, and carbohydrates—make up the unique structure of protoplasm. They formed, aided by the high temperatures of the water, out of the smaller organic molecules of the ocean. After some millions of years, their concentration in the ocean may have been as high as 1 per cent.

Under some conditions giant molecules exert attractive forces on each other which may result in the forming of microscopic-sized droplets of more concentrated material out of the dilute solution of the ocean. Most of these droplets soon broke up, but some of them, by chance, consisted of more stable combinations. Such droplets are known to have the capacity of absorbing materials from their surroundings, and since the medium in which these droplets formed contained the chemicals of which they were themselves composed, they could grow by absorption.

The chemical structure of each droplet was completely random, and the probability of any droplet having the right chemical composition to allow it to absorb materials was extremely small. But because there were so many droplets, it must have happened occasionally. The wrong combinations disintegrated and returned their substance to the ocean, but the others grew. Eventually they got so large that they became physically unstable and broke into small fragments, which could then grow on their own. We must confess that this concept of physical instability is no explanation. Even today, we have no real understanding of the forces that pull cells in half.

Natural selection was already operating in the evolutionary process of the droplets. The successful combinations multiplied and populated the oceans, while the unsuccessful ones, the vast majority, degenerated. But in the very act of multiplying, they imposed new conditions that they had to meet for their survival, for they would soon use up all the available chemicals from the ocean. Since there is always a certain instability in these droplets, cutting off the supply of building materials will cause them to fall apart. Here and there, there was a droplet whose particular chemical structure made it possible for it to produce a small chemical change, to take in a useless molecule and alter it slightly to make it fit the requirements of the droplet. Assimilation had begun. And again selection operated, for the droplet that could do this had a supply of raw materials denied to the others. The assimilating aggregates could now multiply, while the others must inevitably disintegrate. As time passed, the droplets developed ever-more-complex chemical systems to make use of progressively simpler molecules. This process removed the larger molecules from the ocean and concentrated them in the cells—if we can call them that—continuing down the scale of molecular size until the organic material of the ocean was largely pre-empted by the cells. As the primordial food supply disappeared, life would have come to an end before it was well under way unless some entirely new method of nutrition came into being.

NEW KINDS OF FOOD

The droplets we have been discussing bear little resemblance to anything that exists today. The thin, hot soup does not exist any more, and a cell whose only method of nutrition is to absorb organic matter from its surroundings and alter it slightly would not survive. Oparin surmised that as organic food became increasingly scarce, new nutritional habits evolved, methods that could use simpler chemicals. Even today, there are bacteria that nourish themselves on hydrogen sulfide, iron, alcohol, or nitrites. These are minor byroads of evolution; the large body of living things divided very early into two main groups.

Sometime during the process of depleting the organic chemicals, a cell developed the ability to absorb another, thereby increasing its size. Suppose the proteins of the ingested particle were unsuitable? Then a chemical system making digestion possible would have a high survival value. The assimilation mechanism already existed. If to this we added a mechanism to break down foreign proteins into the simpler form that can be assimilated, then the elements of the animal type of nutrition are all present.

Animal nutrition is always destructive to life as a whole. Only a small part of the material eaten is assimilated; the rest supplies energy to keep the life processes going, and is thereby degraded into wastes. The large, organic molecules, built up over so many millions of years, were gradually being broken up into useless forms such as carbon dioxide. Unless some new method evolved by which organic molecules could be quickly and continuously rebuilt from the wastes in the ocean, life would soon come to an end, having accomplished nothing more interesting than converting the carbides of the crust into carbon dioxide in the atmosphere.

The substance that saved life was *chlorophyll.* This material made possible the continuous recycling of the world's carbon by making active hydrogen available. Chlorophyll can use the sun's energy to separate the hydrogen of water from the oxygen. The oxygen is released, and the hydrogen can then be combined with carbon dioxide to form sugar. Carbon is once again in usable form in a large molecule containing stored energy which was supplied by the sun. With the sun's energy to keep the cycle going, carbon can then be rebuilt into organic chemicals, which are the food of the living creatures of the world. Since the coming of the first green plant, the increase of life on earth has been limited only by the availability of suitable space.

The genealogy of living creatures at this early stage is much in doubt. There is good evidence, as we shall see in Chapter 3, that today's animals evolved from the same tiny, green, free-swimming cells as did the modern plants. Therefore it does not seem likely that the animals of the world are direct descendants of the first droplet-eating droplets, except by way of the green plants. There are animals and plants today that live by absorbing organic chemicals, but these are either parasitic, or they live where there is active decay. Since they depend on a higher form of life for their food, they are clearly not left over from the thin, hot soup. They have evolved from typical plants and animals by losing their digestive or photosynthetic ability. It is possible that the bacteria are a truly primitive group. They have a wide range of methods of nutrition, wider than all other creatures of the world combined. In the early days, many different methods of getting nourishment from simple chemicals must have evolved. Perhaps many of these survive in the bacteria, while only one—*photosynthesis,* which is the making of carbohydrates by chlorophyll in the presence of light—succeeded so well that it gave rise to the green plants and, through them, to the animals.

The green plants created profound changes in the world and its life. Apparently, from them evolved animals, which replaced the animal-like droplets in the sea. The atmosphere changed; animals released carbon dioxide into it, which plants used. The use of this carbon dioxide by the plants resulted in a release of free oxygen, which for the first time became a large component of the atmosphere. This free oxygen in turn resulted in a number of changes. Both plants and animals developed mechanisms for using this oxygen for oxidation of their food, giving them an energy-producing system far superior to any that had existed before, thus making possible the evolution of active animals. Various bacteria began to produce energy by combining this free oxygen with materials such as ammonia, hydrogen sulfide, sulfur, carbonates, methane, and carbon monoxide. One result was the disappearance of ammonia from the atmosphere, the nitrogen of the ammonia molecule being released to form the main part of today's atmosphere.

The broad outlines of this process of origin of life are now widely accepted, but a great many problems remain. Since Oparin's theory was first published, it has been found that self-reproduction is a property of nucleic acids, not of proteins, as was then supposed. Did life pass through a virus-like stage in which free nucleic acid molecules created copies of themselves out of the materials of the soup? If so, how did this process result in cells? If not, how did the viruses originate, and how did the original globules reproduce? Like any good piece of scientific work, Oparin's theory created more problems than it solved.

So we come back at last to the idea that life originated spontaneously from nonliving matter. But not in a few days from a dirty shirt. It took millions, or more likely billions, of years, and could not conceivably have happened in a shorter period of time. Most biologists today believe that, under today's conditions, a new genesis of life from nonliving matter only is impossible. The oxygen in the atmosphere blocks out most of the ultraviolet light that is needed to produce the simple organic molecules. There are not enough small-sized, organic chemicals produced by decay and possibly also formed anew from the remaining carbides in the crust, and there is no enormous cauldron to cook them in. The temperatures of the ocean are too low to stimulate polymerization at any reasonable rate. And if the early steps could be taken, the oxygen in the atmosphere would react with the small organic molecules, so that they would tend to be destroyed rather than built. Furthermore, the bacteria in the world today are capable of using practically any kind of organic material for food; it is unlikely that any could escape for long. Life changes the world, and in doing so destroys the conditions necessary for its own genesis.

Can Life Exist Somewhere Else?

Since man first realized that his home, the Earth, is only an infinitesimal speck in an enormous universe, he has speculated on the possibility that other living creatures might exist on other planets. Until fairly recently, it was generally believed that the formation of a solar system around a star —like our system of planets orbiting the sun—is a rare event, so unlikely that it might not have happened more than once in the entire universe. Until Oparin's great work, many believed that the origin of life on earth was the result of an almost miraculous combination of events, a strictly fortuitous combination of chemicals that might never have happened. Since life depended on two such highly unlikely occurrences, it was believed that the earth is probably unique in the universe, that no other life exists anywhere else.

In the past twenty years, this position has been completely reversed. It is now thought highly likely that not only life, but intelligent life at a higher technological level than ours exists at many places in the universe. This is a bold idea, a position that no one would care to take without good reason. And yet respectable scientists are seriously discussing methods of establishing contact with other worlds and two men have already made the first attempt! It has become increasingly difficult to know where competent scientific speculation leaves off and science-fiction begins.

One important reason for this about-face was Oparin's theory. He showed the world how to view the origin of life not as an almost impossible accident, but as a necessary result of natural law. Wherever conditions are right, we can expect that the same sequence of events that produced the planet-wide evolution of life on earth would produce the same result on other planets. It comes, then, to a question of how many planets in the universe have possessed the appropriate conditions for a sufficiently long period of time.

The first condition necessary for life is the appropriate temperature. Pluto is nearly at absolute zero, while the interior of the sun has a temperature of many millions of degrees. Of this great range of temperatures, life is possible in only a very narrow band. One of the immutable laws of chemistry is that chemical reactions speed up with an increase in temperature. A living structure of any kind represents a delicate balance between stability of structure and continuous chemical change. If the temperature gets too high, the delicate cellular structure necessary for the life processes cannot persist. If it gets too low, the chemical processes would become too slow to keep the machinery going. On this ground alone, we can be sure that life is restricted to those parts of the universe that fall within a fairly narrow temperature range.

Most scientists who have written in this area feel that we can restrict the possible temperature range even further, that life can exist only where there is liquid water. This places the limits at 0°C and about 100°C, depending on pressure. Water is the reaction medium and solvent in cells, and the chemistry of proteins, nucleic acids, carbohydrates, and fats can only take place in liquid water. If the water freezes, the dissolved molecules are unable to move around into contact with each other, and the chemical reactions stop. If the water is vaporized, it is impossible to maintain such structures as membranes within the cell.

But how do we know that there is not, on some other

planet, life based on a completely different kind of chemistry than ours? Do we know enough about chemistry to speculate on this question? We do. There can be no reasonable doubt that the 101 natural and artificial elements that are known on earth are identical with those that make up all other matter in the universe. We know enough about the fundamental particles that make up atoms to realize that they can be combined only in certain ways. It is possible that atoms heavier than our 101 exist, but if they do, they last no more than a fraction of a second, and so cannot contribute to living structure.

This conclusion has been verified experimentally, for analysis of the light coming from a star can tell us what elements are present in the star. The stars are made of the same basic stuff as you and me. We can make only one possible exception to these conclusions: a system of elements made of "anti-matter" is possible, and if it exists, we could not distinguish its light emissions from those of ordinary matter. But anti-matter would have to obey the same chemical laws as ordinary matter, and the same temperature limitations would apply.

Well, then, we have a particular set of elements to work with. Out of this set, is it possible to conceive of a form of life with a chemistry very different from ours? To begin with, life is necessarily an extremely complex process; no simple chemical system could take in materials from its surroundings, convert them chemically into usable material, use part of them as a source of energy, and assimilate the rest. A system that can do all this is inconceivable without giant molecules. Of all the elements, carbon is unique in its ability to form large molecules made of long chains of atoms. When nitrogen and oxygen are included in these chains, a single chain of atoms many thousands of atoms long can be formed, and this is how the giant molecules of proteins and nucleic acids are built. Only one other element —silicon—can form similar chains, but no one has ever found a way to make the chains very long because the silicon atom is too large. It is almost certain that life, wherever it exists, is based on compounds of carbon.

It is less certain that proteins and nucleic acids are indispensable in forming a self-reproducing system. The fact that no chemist has been able to suggest another system that would work proves nothing, for they could not have invented the protein-nucleic acid system either! It is quite probable that any planet with an original atmosphere of ammonia and water, and a crust similar to the earth's, would develop the same general kind of protein-nucleic acid system of life that we have on earth. Some chemists believe that no other kind of system is possible, although it has been suggested that a planet with far less oxygen than we possess might form a system with liquid ammonia as the solvent and reaction medium rather than water, Although this would require lower temperatures and higher pressures than we have on earth, it is certainly within the range of possibility.

Life in the Universe

The search for life in the rest of the universe, then, becomes the search for appropriate conditions. In the solar system, temperature is the chief problem, since all the planets appear to have a common origin and, therefore, the same chemical composition. Mercury, and probably Venus also, are too hot, while Jupiter and the rest of the solar system are too cold. The asteroids and most of the satellites are so small that their gravitation is not strong enough to prevent water from evaporating into space. There is some evidence for life on Mars, as there are large regions that turn green in the spring and brown in the fall. These could easily be some form of vegetation. There is oxygen in the atmosphere, which probably means that there is plant life. But Mars is smaller than the Earth, and is very dry. It is quite possible that Mars is a dying planet, where life once existed but is gradually coming to an end as the vital water is lost into space.

How about other stars? Astronomers tell us that there are at least one hundred billion billion stars in the universe, about as many as the grains of sand on all the beaches of the world. We used to think that the solar system resulted from the gravitational attraction of two stars passing quite close to each other. The average distance between stars is so great that this probably has happened only a few times in the history of the universe. So it was thought that our solar system is unique and that few, if any, other stars are surrounded by planets. In the 1920's, evidence was found that there are probably many solar systems. Methods were discovered for determining the rate at which the stars rotate, and many stars, including the sun, were found to rotate much more slowly than the average rate. If all stars originally have the same spin, a large part of the spin must have been carried off in the formation of a system of planets. We have not been able to see these planets, but there is some hope that we will very soon, with a telescope orbiting the earth far above the interference produced by our atmosphere.

There is additional evidence for the existence of other solar systems. A star surrounded by planets would be expected to wobble a little, due to the weight of the planets. In May of 1963, the first direct evidence of another solar system was found when wobbling was detected in a nearby star.

The evidence that other stars have planets, plus other information, has led to new theories of the origin of the solar system. Much is now known about the changes that take place in a star as it grows older. A majority of stars belong to a group called the "main sequence stars." Among this group, to which our sun belongs, all differences are due to two factors: the age of the star and the amount of material in it when it was born. It now seems that *any* main sequence star that starts out about the same size as the sun would have to form, at a certain stage in its life, a system of planets. Further, one theory holds that this system of planets would have to be much like the solar system, containing about the same number of planets. These would be similar in size, distance from the star, and even chemical composition to those of the solar system. If this theory is correct, there must be many solar systems identical to ours and, therefore, many earths.

It now appears that at least one star out of every thousand is surrounded by a system of planets. Even if these systems are not alike, probably at least one out of every thousand has a planet at the right distance from its star so that its temperature will sustain liquid water. Perhaps one in a thousand of these is large enough to retain its water and an atmosphere, and small enough so that the surface pressures are not prohibitive. Any of these planets with the correct size and temperature could be expected to produce nucleic-acid-protein life, provided only that they possessed an atmosphere containing ammonia and water, and rocks containing carbon—and at least one out of every thousand should fulfill this condition. Dividing the number of stars in the universe by one thousand, four times, gives us a figure of *at least* one hundred thousand planets in the universe that could support the type of life we know on earth! If there are other chemical combinations that permit life to exist, the amount of life in the universe may be much larger.

Naturally one would not expect the living creatures of other worlds to look like those we see around us, but their chemical processes would probably be very similar. Given enough time, it is almost certain that some form of intelligent life would develop. It might take other planets a little longer or a little shorter period of time to pass from a hot cauldron to a society based on technology than it did on earth. We may therefore assume that some of the other planets possess cultures considerably in advance of our own.

We have already made an attempt to establish contact with intelligent beings outside our solar system. If there were any possibility of such contact, it would have to be with a civilization at least as advanced as our own. Since our most powerful radio transmitters can now send a signal that could be detected by our most sensitive receivers at a distance of ten light years, we must assume that communication at that distance is possible. Two stars within that distance are of the right type to have had a planetary system for a sufficiently long period for intelligent life to develop.

One of the most sensitive radio receivers in the world, the giant radio telescope at Green Bank, West Virginia, was pointed at these stars for a few days in 1960. Of course it is necessary to guess what frequency to tune to and what to listen for. The radio telescope itself was designed for reception to a wave length of 21 cm., because this frequency is produced by hydrogen atoms throughout space and it was this frequency that the astronomers wished to study. It was assumed that another civilization would also possess telescopes tuned to this frequency, and that the intelligent inhabitants of distant planets would naturally think of transmitting very close to this frequency. As to the nature of the signal, any ordered series of pulses or signals would indicate an intelligent broadcaster, perhaps a series representing the ordinal numbers: one, two, three, four, etc. If a signal were received, it would have been sent ten years previously, for it would take that long for the signal to travel the distance.

No signals were heard, and the test was abandoned after a few days.

In November of 1961 a group of scientists held a conference at Green Bank on the subject of life on other worlds. One report estimated that there ought to be intelligent life somewhere within a thousand light years of us. As our receivers become more sensitive, this volume of space will have to be explored for signals. One difficulty will be the time lapse. If it takes a thousand years for signals to reach us and another thousand for an answer, we cannot expect to hold friendly conversations. We cannot know what is happening on the other planet now, but only what happened a thousand years ago! These scientists believe that sooner or later we must hear someone out there, who may already be trying to talk to us.

3

The Evolution of Sex

The word "reproduction," as used here, has a broad meaning. It encompasses all those processes by which life begets life, including the events that occur when a single cell becomes two and even those processes occurring within a single cell by which new living matter is created within the cell. But the word is commonly used in a much narrower sense to mean the processes by which new organisms are created. To most people, in fact, the word "reproduction" conjures up a still-narrower picture, an image of a sequence of events that begins with the union of a male and a female and is followed by pregnancy and birth. In fact, however, our reproductive habits are distinctly unusual.

There is one feature of the human generative process that is widespread in nature, occurring at least sometimes in the reproductive processes of most creatures. This is fertilization—the union of a sperm with an egg. This is such a fundamental part of our understanding of reproduction today that it is difficult to realize that it was not until 1875 that the nature of the process was understood. The fact that a new individual starts its existence at the instant that a single sperm cell from a male enters a single egg cell of a female could not be demonstrated until the science of microscopy had reached a high level.

Fertilization is not reproduction. If anything, it is the reverse, for the result of fertilization is one cell where two existed before. In all organisms, reproduction is founded on the division of cells. Fertilization is actually an interruption of reproduction, an interlude in which the repeated division of cells is halted while two cells unite. As we will see later, fertilization has an important function, but a great many organisms reproduce without it, either always or occasionally.

ASEXUAL REPRODUCTIVE PROCESSES

In most one-celled creatures, the Protozoa and many of the algae, division of the cell is the same thing as reproduction of the organism. They reproduce simply by splitting in half (Figure 3-1).

FIGURE 3-1. Binary fission—asexual reproduction of *Ameba*.

Every many-celled creature grows by reproduction of its cells, a process similar to the reproduction of the one-celled organisms. Every gardener knows that he can use this process to make new plants; a section of a rose stem or the leaf of an African violet will form roots and grow into a separate organism. Many multi-celled organisms make use of this regenerative ability in nature to reproduce without sexual means. The tiny flatworm known as *Planaria* simply splits transversely when it has grown inconveniently large.

Some of the tiny nemertine worms that live in soil may break up into a hundred or more tiny pieces, each of which becomes a new worm.

This crude fragmentation is not the usual method of asexual reproduction. The polyp *Hydra* (Figure 3-2) forms buds that grow into new individuals and swim away. Many plants, such as the strawberry, grow special stems that lie on the ground and produce new plants at intervals. Most grasses spread by extensive systems of underground stems, binding the soil into turf. Other plants will sprout from spreading roots, from stems that touch the ground, from broken sections of stem floating in a stream, or even from leaves blown away by the wind.

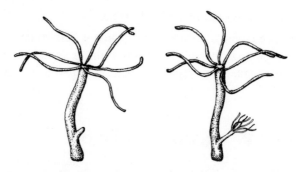

FIGURE 3-2. Formation and growth of a *Hydra* bud.

Nearly all plants form special asexual reproductive cells called "spores." In many of the green algae, such as *Chlamydomonas* (Figure 3-3), these take the form of tiny cells swimming through the water by means of whiplike flagella. These are called "zoospores" because they look like tiny animals. They settle down in a likely spot and grow into an adult, serving both to reproduce the organism and to distribute the species to new areas.

Land plants produce a different kind of spore, tiny thick-walled cells that are carried as dust in the air. They

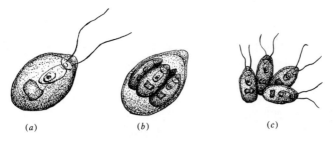

FIGURE 3-3. Formation of zoospores in *Chlamydomonas:* (*a*) adult; (*b*) zoospores forming; (*c*) mature zoospores.

are formed in special spore cases (Figure 3-4), which may be the little cylindrical structures of mosses, the tiny dots on the back of fern leaves, or the anthers of flowers. Spores are so numerous that they make up a significant fraction of dust in the air; a single bracket fungus may release millions of spores into the air every day for several years. Spores are a characteristic feature of plant reproduction, found in most plants but in an insignificant number of animals.

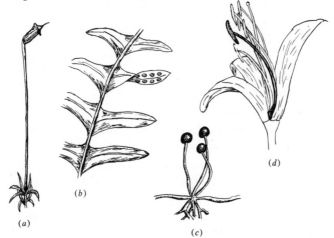

FIGURE 3-4. Various spore cases: (*a*) moss; (*b*) fern; (*c*) mold; (*d*) anther of a flower.

THE USEFULNESS OF SEX

Sex is a complicated process that interrupts the repeated reproduction of cells. A process this many-sided and complex must have arisen through a long evolutionary history, in the trial and error of millions of individuals through countless generations. Since sexual reproduction is so widespread, the law of natural selection implies with absolute certainty that, for some reason, a species that reproduces sexually has a better chance of survival than a similar species in which each individual has a single parent.

The mystery of the usefulness of sex remained unsolved until biologists learned to stop thinking of evolution in terms of individuals and began to consider populations. In a stable environment, a willow tree produced from a twig that broke off and floated downstream is no better off than one produced from seed. The advantages of sexual reproduction are felt only in the long run, for it is the species as a whole that benefits, not the individual.

Each species exists in a state of balance with its environment. A species survives because it is exquisitely adapted to a particular set of conditions—certain temperatures, light conditions, humidity, soil content, parasites, predators, food organisms, and so on. In the long run, the survival of a species depends on its ability to get along in a variety of environments. Compare, for example, the raccoon and the koala (the Australian "teddy bear"). Raccoons eat a wide variety of soft foods—fruits, frogs, insects, small mammals, etc.—and live practically anywhere there are trees, from woodlands high on the slopes of mountains to wooded swamps near the shore. The koala eats only the leaves of the eucalyptus tree. If the climate of the earth were to change, the eucalyptus forests where the koala lives might be wiped out, and the koalas along with them. The change might wipe out many of the usable habitats of the raccoon, but it is unlikely to eliminate them all.

In a large and wide-ranging species such as the raccoon, there is always a certain amount of variability, so that there will be many individuals far worse adapted to the environment than the average. This variability is necessary for the survival of the species, for when conditions change, the "worse" suddenly become better. If all individuals were alike, a single dry season, for example, might wipe out the species. But if there is variation, there will very likely be some individuals for whom the new environment is not fatal. It is these variant members of the species that carry on when the environment undergoes a change. Without them, any species is sooner or later doomed.

The amount of variation in a species has much to do with its method of reproduction. An individual produced asexually will be nearly identical to its parent. If a species reproduces asexually only, the extreme members, less well adapted to the environment, will eventually be eliminated, and the species becomes more uniform as time goes by. This is the road to extinction, for a change in the environment will wipe out the whole species.

Now we can see how sexual reproduction confers an advantage on a species. If each individual has two parents, he will not be exactly like either one, but will have some properties of both. The recombination of heredities that ushers in each new generation assures that there will always be variation in the population. Now if the climate changes or a food species disappears, there will be some individuals who find the new conditions to their liking and will be able to carry on. Sex maintains the variations within the species, making the species as a whole more adaptable to new conditions. It is for this reason that the sexual process with all its complexity has become part of the reproductive cycle of most animals and plants.

THE ORIGIN OF SEX

A process that involves many special structures and behavior patterns, as does sex, could not originate full-blown, but must have evolved gradually. Although we know that sexual differentiation evolved gradually, we cannot study this evolution directly, for it occurred many millions of years ago. We do not even have fossils to guide us, for there are no fossils that old. Our only clues to the origin of sexuality come indirectly, from study of primitive plants and animals in which simple forms of sexual reproduction still exist.

Sexual reproduction might have begun in some such plant as *Chlamydomonas.* You will recall that this single-celled green alga forms zoospores, tiny replicas of itself, by subdivision of its own body. Sometimes, however, the parent cell breaks down still further to convert itself into a large number of still smaller cells (Figure 3-5). These are *gametes,* or sex cells. They are not capable of growing directly into adults, but must first unite together in pairs to form a *zygote* (which means, simply, a cell formed by the union of two gametes). The zygote survives the winter, and then divides into four zoospores, each of which can grow into an

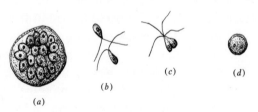

FIGURE 3-5: Sexual reproduction in *Chlamydomonas:* (*a*) gametes forming within parent cell; (*b*) gametes approaching each other; (*c*) gametes fusing; (*d*) young zygote.

adult. The sexual process is quite primitive, for all the gametes are alike, differing little from ordinary zoospores. The conclusion seems inescapable that, in this line at least, sexual reproduction originated as a modification of asexual reproduction by zoospores.

The union of two similar gametes as in *Chlamydomonas* may not seem to be a sex process, for there is no difference between male and female. But some of the other green algae do have this additional complication. In some species of *Oedogonium* (Figure 3-6), a green alga composed of long, filamentous colonies, there are two kinds of sex cells. Certain small, flat cells produce two small swimming gametes each. These have many flagella and are similar to the zoospores in this species. In another part of the filament is a large gamete, a primordial egg containing a food supply for the germinating zygote. A crack in its cell wall admits a swimming gamete, a sperm, which fertilizes it. Later on, the zygote escapes and divides into four zoospores, which grow into new filaments the following spring.

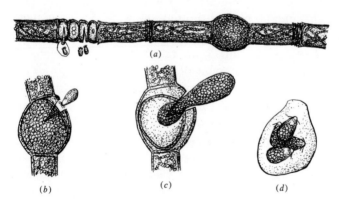

FIGURE 3-6. Sexual reproduction in *Oedogonium:* (*a*) sperms escaping and an egg in place; (*b*) fertilization; (*c*) the zygote escaping; (*d*) the four zoospores.

This is the beginning of the differentiation of the sexes. Other green algae demonstrate later stages, for there are green algae in which the eggs are very large and sperms consist of little but nucleus and flagella. In many forms, the two kinds of gametes are produced on different plants, which are thus the male and the female. The sexes can be distinguished easily, for the two kinds of gametes are made in different kinds of sex organs. It is possible to trace the evolution of sexual reproduction from the primitive form in which the two cells hardly differ from zoospores to complex plants with a high degree of differentiation into male and female, all within the green algae.

The differentiation of the sexes into two kinds is an extra complication, added to the originally simpler sex process. It has been enormously successful, for today only an occasional species forms only one kind of gamete. Once again, evolutionary principles tell us that in some way there is advantage to a species in being differentiated into two sexes. A zygote must store a certain amount of food to get the new generation started. There is a limit to the size of cell that can be pushed through the water by a few flagella, so not much food storage is possible in a swimming gamete. If the swimming function is restricted to one gamete, there is no limit to the amount of food that can be stored in the other. It is this separation of the swimming and food storage functions that defines the difference between an egg and a sperm; this, in turn distinguishes male from female.

How did sex get started among animals? The logical place to look for the origins of animal sexuality is the group of one-celled animals called *flagellates*. These tiny animals are closely related to the green flagellates like *Chlamydomonas*. They look like swimming green algae that have lost their chlorophyll and thick cellulose coats. Like the green flagellates, they can survive by absorbing organic matter from the water in which they live. But some of them can also perform the typically animal process of taking in and digesting solid food. They seem to represent survivals of the earliest animals, apparently derived from green flagellates. Perhaps the sex process in animals was inherited from green flagellate ancestors, which would mean that it evolved only once.

Unfortunately this neat answer does not seem to be correct. There is no sex process of any kind in the animal flagellates. This is not conclusive, for it might have existed at first and been lost in the billions of years of evolution that separate today's animal flagellates from their green ancestors. There is a stronger reason for believing that the sex process arose independently at least once in the evolution of animals.

Whenever divisions and unions of cells are studied, it is important to understand what happens to the *chromosomes.* These structures are long, thin, tangled threads within the cell nucleus. As we will see in Chapter 9, they can easily be counted during cell division, when they turn into short, fat rods. The number of chromosomes in every cell is crucial. Every *Chlamydomonas* cell, for example, has exactly 191 chromosomes. They are all different from each other, and they constitute what is called a *set* of chromosomes. When a cell divides, each chromosome splits precisely in half, and one-half goes into each of the daughter cells, so that every daughter cell has a full set. At fertilization, two sets of chromosomes enter the same cell, the zygote. In spite of the many variations in the sexual process, one basic principle is never violated: gametes have one set of chromosomes and zygotes have two sets. A cell with one set of chromosomes is said to be *haploid*; if there are two sets, the cell is *diploid*.

In *Chlamydomonas,* the diploid phase lasts only for the

life of the zygote. In the spring when the zygote germinates, it undergoes the process of *reduction division* (see Chapter 9). In this process, a diploid cell divides twice to form four haploid ones. These are zoospores, which swim away to grow up into haploid adults. Higher plants have much more complicated life cycles, but it is nearly always true that reduction division produces spores. In animals, the situation is quite different. The animal body is diploid. Reduction division takes place in ovaries or testes and results in haploid gametes. There is no reduction division of the zygote, which grows into a diploid adult. Because this pattern is so different from that in plants, it is unlikely that the sexual reproduction found in animals evolved from that in plants.

The question of the origins of the sexual process has recently been complicated by the discovery of sexuality in bacteria. It was noted some years ago that if two strains of a given species of bacteria, differing by two characteristics, are cultured together on the same plate, it is sometimes possible to obtain a new strain in which the characteristics of the two parent strains are combined. This clearly implies some kind of sexual process. With that invaluable instrument, the electron microscope, thin strands connecting two bacteria together have been found. This seems to be some kind of sexual process, perhaps similar to the exchange of nuclei that is known in certain protozoa. The evolutionary relationships of the bacteria are in doubt, and we may never know how the sex life of a bacterium is related to that of animals and plants, if it is at all.

More Efficient Fertilization

In many ocean creatures—starfishes, marine worms, many fishes—the egg is fertilized in the open water. There must always be some mechanism to insure that eggs and sperms are released near each other, or else the chances of fertilization would be slim. In many fishes, the mechanism is an instinctive behavior pattern of some kind. A male ready to mate approaches a female with a special kind of swimming motion, perhaps simultaneously presenting her with a special signal, such as a brightly colored pattern. If the fish is indeed a female, of the right species and ready for mating, she responds with some special movement of her own. For some time both partners perform a stereotyped dance, each movement of one evoking a response from the other. If either one misses a cue, the dance stops. The courtship dance ends with the female discharging her eggs and the male covering them with sperms. There will rarely be any confusion of species, for other kinds of fishes do not know the same movement.

Courtship dances of this kind are found in many different organisms, but they always seem to have the same two functions: to identify the other individual as to species, sex, and breeding condition, and to stimulate the other to mate. All sorts of sensory signals are used: the bright colors of birds, the flashing lights of a firefly or a luminous fish, the croaking of a frog, the hammering of a woodpecker, the yowl of a cat, the characteristic odor of a moth. In many cases, courtship culminates in direct contact between the partners. A male lobster clasps the female and deposits his sperms on her shell, right near the opening of her oviducts, so that the eggs are fertilized as they pass out of her body. A male frog mounts the back of the female and squeezes her, forcing the eggs out while he drops his sperms on them as they emerge.

At a still higher stage, the sperms are injected into the body of the female and fertilize the eggs internally. Often the developing young are kept within the body of the female until they are ready to move about on their own. In reptiles and birds there is a single body opening just below the base of the tail, leading into an organ called the "cloaca." The cloaca receives the waste products of the intestines and the kidneys, as well as the eggs of the female or the sperms of the male. After courtship, the male mounts the female. The tail of the female then turns so as to bring the two cloacal openings into contact, and the sperms pass from the cloaca of the male into that of the female. The eggs, without a shell, have already passed out of the ovary into the oviduct (Figure 3-7), and fertilization occurs here.

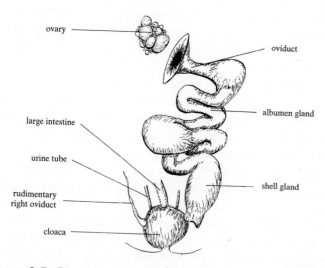

ovary

oviduct

large intestine

albumen gland

urine tube

rudimentary right oviduct

shell gland

cloaca

FIGURE 3-7. Reproductive organs of a female bird with two eggs in oviduct.

After fertilization, the eggs continue to pass down the oviduct, where the albumen layers (egg white), membranes, and shell are added by special glands. In birds and most reptiles, eggs are laid several days afterward. Internal fertilization is necessary if the egg is to be laid in a dry place, for unless the egg is in water, it needs a shell to protect it from drying out. Sperms could not penetrate the shell, so the egg must be fertilized before the shell forms.

Internal fertilization has developed independently in many different evolutionary lines and is found today in such diverse creatures as insects, flatworms, sharks, and many unrelated bony fishes, as well as reptiles, birds, and mammals. In many of these lines, no shell is formed, and the young are kept inside the mother for long periods of time. The young are carried internally until they are ready to move about in sharks, in many flies, in garter snakes, in such "livebearing" fishes as the guppy and swordbill, and in all placental mammals. The sea horse, which looks like a knight escaped from a chess set, is unique, for in this species the male carries the young in a special pouch under his abdomen.

In many evolutionary lines, the male has developed a special organ with which to deliver his sperms, a *penis*. The penis of a male duck enables him to mate in the water. Similar organs are found in such unrelated forms as flatworms, snails, insects, turtles, and mammals.

In some creatures, the connection between male and female becomes permanent. The flatworms called *Diplozoon,* which live as parasites on the gills of minnows, unite together in pairs as they grow up. One member grows male organs, the other becomes a female, and the two remain in contact for life. This is surely the furthest limit to which togetherness can be carried, and one can only hope that they are happy together. In such forms as angler fish, barnacles, and rotifers, the male is reduced to a tiny parasite living inside his mate.

PROTECTION OF THE YOUNG

Fertilization is a beginning, and the zygote has a long and difficult road to travel before it is an adult. A starfish embryo uses up its stored food in a few days and must care for itself from then on; you, on the other hand, were carried, fed, and protected in a warm bath for nine months, supplied with an ideal diet of milk for several months after that, and then introduced to a variety of foods carefully prepared by a loving mother for many years. During all this time, you were a constant drain on the time, emotions, patience, energy, and finances of two doting parents. These are two extreme cases; other animals form a wide spectrum of patterns in between.

Most marine animals lay small eggs containing little food. The eggs hatch into tiny young that must fend for themselves while they are still almost or quite microscopic. A newly hatched mackerel, a fraction of an inch long, dines on microscopic living creatures and grows into a fish that hunts and eats other fishes. The newly hatched animals often bear no resemblance to the adults and live a different kind of life. The microscopic larva of a starfish could hardly be expected to feed by using brute force—as its parents do— to separate the shells of an oyster and then devour the contents. The surface layers of the ocean contain countless larvae of marine worms, acorn worms, sea urchins, and shrimplike crustaceans, all feeding on the one-celled green plants that float in the water. Most of them look nothing at all like their parents.

For many creatures of the ocean, these free-swimming larvae have another important function. Sponges, barnacles, sea squirts, clams, and tube-dwelling worms spend their entire adult lives fixed in one position, and the swimming larvae serve as a means of spreading the species. This is also important for many parasites, for the larvae of gill-parasitic flatworms must find another fish before they can settle down. Usually most of the growth is accomplished in the larval stage, and this is nearly always the case with insects.

The codling moth lays eggs in apple blossoms; while the eggs are maturing, the blossom grows into an apple. The "worm" in the apple is the mature larva.

If the egg is large enough, it contains enough food so that it can hatch into a good-sized baby, thereby eliminating the larval stage. A bird's egg is a great deal larger than those of the marine animals we have been discussing. The difference in size is entirely a matter of food stored in the form of yolk in the egg proper and albumen deposited around the egg. The living matter in a hen's egg is microscopic, just as it is in the egg of a starfish.

Even in the water, not all eggs are left to make out as best they can. The stickleback, a tiny fish found in European creeks and ditches, builds a nest of aquatic grasses, and the male guards the eggs until they hatch. The nests of birds are well known, but lungfishes, millipedes, and some snakes such as the copperhead also build nests and guard their eggs. Many creatures carry their eggs until they hatch—in the cocoon that a cockroach carries around, attached to the appendages of a lobster, in the puffy skin of the back of the Surinam toad, in the mouth of the Egyptian mouth-breeding fish. A pair of penguins take turns in carrying their single egg, holding it on their feet and keeping it warm against the belly.

As we have seen, many kinds of females fail to lay the egg after it has been fertilized, keeping it inside until it is well developed. One species of flatworm carries this process to absurd lengths, for the embryo, while still in the mother's uterus, matures and produces eggs which develop without fertilization. The young worm is born pregnant! The ultimate development of the internal care of the young is achieved in the mammals. In this group, to which we belong, the egg is extremely small. (The human egg contains only enough food for five days, and a whale's egg is smaller than a hummingbird's.) After it is fertilized, the egg passes into the uterus and becomes fastened to the uterus wall. The wall grows around it, so that it is completely surrounded by the nourishing and oxygen-bearing body fluids of the mother. As the embryo grows larger, it can no longer provide itself with food and oxygen by absorption through the surface; it needs blood to distribute these materials and to carry away the wastes produced in its growing tissues. It forms a circulatory system and blood. It also develops a special organ, the placenta (Figure 3-8) that remains attached to the uterus wall until the baby is born. The baby's blood flows out of its body through the navel into the umbilical cord and from there to the placenta. Here it picks up food and oxygen and discharges waste materials, exchanging these substances with the blood of the mother.

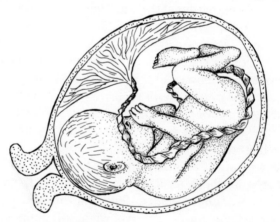

FIGURE 3-8. Human embryo shortly before birth.

There are a few other groups in which a placenta has evolved: some scorpions, certain flies, and a primitive, wormlike arthropod. But the mammals have evolved the most efficient methods of caring for the young. Even after the young are born, feeding by the mother continues, first in the form of milk and later, as a rule, with the same solid foods the parents eat. The strictly human phenomenon of parental love comes from this kind of biological background.

ALTERNATION OF GENERATIONS

Because humans have only one method of reproduction, we tend to assume that this is typical. In most plants and lower animals it is not unusual for the same organism to reproduce both sexually and asexually. A *Hydra* forms buds, but also produces eggs, sperms, or both at certain times of the year. A blackberry forms seeds by a complicated sexual process (of which, more later), and also propagates new plants wherever its drooping branches touch the ground. Asexual methods are simpler and more efficient, as they do not require courtship, mating, and fertilization of the egg. But in the long run, sexual reproduction leads to increased variation and survival of the species.

Some animals and most plants have developed a way of combining the efficiency of asexual reproduction with the guarantee of repeated recombination of chromosomes into new patterns provided by the sex process. This is accomplished by alternating asexual and sexual reproduction in every other generation. In these forms, a fertilized egg always grows into an individual without sex organs. This reproduces asexually to form a sexual organism. The common jellyfish *Aurelia* (Figure 3-9), for example, regularly alternates a sexual with an asexual generation. The familiar umbrella-shaped jellyfish stage is the sexual generation. It is hollow, the central cavity opening to the outside through the "handle," which is split into four tentacles. The body cavity is mainly digestive, but the ovaries of the female or the testes of the male also empty into it. Eggs and sperms pass out of the body through the handle, and fertilization takes place in the open water. The zygote develops into a tiny larva, which swims away and grows into a *Hydra*-like polyp. After living a while in this form, it grows longer and splits off thin, tentacle-bearing plates at the upper end, each of which grows into an adult jellyfish. By following the fertilization with an asexual reproductive phase, each zygote has been converted into many adults.

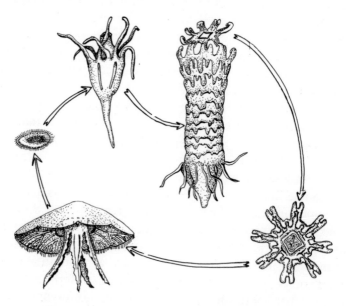

FIGURE 3-9. Life cycle of the jellyfish *Aurelia*.

Among animals, most of the jellyfish-polyp group alternate generations, as do certain parasitic flatworms and protozoa. The malaria parasite has no fewer than seven distinct and different stages that succeed each other in human blood and the mosquito's stomach and salivary glands. One of these stages is sexual. Alternation of generations is the exception in animals; among plants it is the rule. There is a fundamental difference between the two. In animals, both generations are diploid; the fertilized egg grows into an asexual adult which produces sexual animals, and reduction division in this individual produces haploid gametes. In plants, the fertilized egg grows into a diploid organism, as in animals, but there the resemblance stops. The diploid plant forms spores by reduction division. These spores grow into a haploid sexual plant. In practically all plants, the sexual generation is haploid and the asexual generation is diploid.

In some primitive plants, such as the common seaweed *Ulva,* both generations look alike. They are flat sheets, two cells thick and several feet long. The haploid plants produce gametes which swim with two flagella and pair in the open water to form a zygote. The zygote grows into a diploid plant in which some cells undergo reduction division to form haploid zoospores. These, in turn, grow up into the haploid, sexual plant. This situation is unusual, for in most plants one generation is small and lives only long enough to reproduce, while the other is large and lives a long time.

The most primitive green plants above the level of algae are certain small, flat liverworts. These plants have a body like that of a highly organized green alga, but have developed a mass of rootlike structures growing from the lower surface of the body and penetrating into the soft mud on which these plants live (Figure 3-10). *Anthoceros* is a land plant in a sense, although it needs as wet an environment as many green algae. Its plant body is haploid and bears two kinds of sex organs on its upper surface. One consists of a round mass of tissue containing hundreds of cells that eventually develop into biflagellated sperms. These swim through the wet surface of the plant body to reach the other sex organ, a flask-shaped structure containing a single egg at the bottom of a long, hollow neck. The sperm swims down the neck and fertilizes the egg. The zygote grows into an asexual, diploid plant—a stalk partly parasitic on the green leaf that was both father and mother to it.

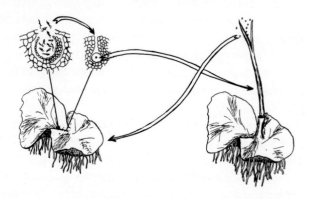

FIGURE 3-10. Life cycle of the liverwort *Anthoceros*.

This stalk is what makes Anthoceros a land plant, for it produces air-borne spores. Give close attention to this insignificant parasite, for it is the ancestor of all flowers and trees, grass and weeds, corn and potatoes.

Other liverworts and mosses are like Anthoceros in that the sexual generation is large and conspicuous, while the asexual generation is a parasite. If you can imagine this spore-bearing plant growing and forming its own roots and leaves, until it becomes large enough to dwarf the sexual plant, you will have a good picture of the reproduction of ferns. In this group, the sexual plant is much like a liverwort and consists of a tiny, heart-shaped leaf lying flat on moist ground (Figure 3-11). The sex organs are found on the lower surface, and water is needed for the sperms to swim through. A little dew is enough. The zygote grows in place, as in a liverwort, but it does not stop at forming a tiny stalk. Instead, it grows very large, forming a diploid plant with dissected green leaves. The sexual plant soon dies, and it is the spore-bearing generation that becomes prominent. Spores are formed in thousands of spore cases on the back of the leaves.

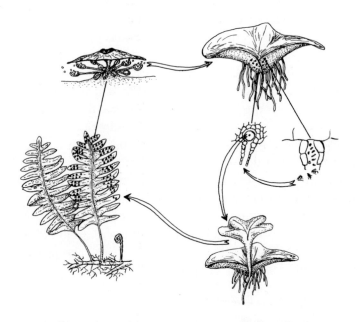

FIGURE 3-11. Life cycle of the fern *Polypodium*.

An additional complication of the reproduction of land plants causes a seeming paradox: sexual differentiation of an asexual plant. *Selaginella* is a tiny plant of wet places that looks at first like a moss, since it consists of tiny leaves arranged in rows along a small stem. But there is a crucial difference. The plant is not haploid like a moss, but diploid. It is spore-bearing and is related to the ferns, not the mosses. The spores are produced on the backs of spore-bearing leaves, dozens of them, which are crowded together at the tips of the stems to form a conelike structure.

Here is the paradox: there are two kinds of spore cases. In one kind, all cells but one degenerate after reduction division, and the one that remains grows into a large spore that fills the whole spore case. In the other kind of spore case, many tiny spores grow. Both kinds of spores germinate while still in the spore case. The large ones grow into a tiny, parasitic, female plant consisting of only a few cells, one of which is the egg. The small spores become male plants, consisting almost entirely of sex organs that produce many sperm. The sperms swim to the eggs, and the zygote, still enclosed in the spore wall of its grandparent, is carried away by the wind. The sexual generation has been reduced to a tiny, parasitic plant. This is exactly the reverse of the situation in the mosses, where the spore-bearing generation is parasitic. In contrast to the ferns, the male and female organs are on separate plants. Furthermore, they have conferred their sexual differentiation on the preceding, asexual generation, for the male and female plants are produced by two different kinds of spores.

FLOWERING PLANTS

When the reproduction of flowering plants was first investigated, it was described as a straightforward sexual process, no different in essentials from the familiar pattern found in animals. Not until the lower plants were well known was it realized that the flowering plants have a complex kind of alternation of generations. The sexual plants have become microscopic parasites as in *Selaginella,* and their differentiation has been pushed back into the preceding generation. Thus a "female" date palm is not female at all; it is a tree that reproduces asexually. It makes tiny spores that grow into female plants in which the eggs are produced. The "male" date palm is structurally different from the "female" because it produces different kinds of spores, spores that grow into microscopic male plants.

A flower is actually a cluster of highly specialized leaves, some of which bear spores. In a typical flower (Figure 3-12), the centermost leaves are fleshy and wound into a cylindrical form. One or several leaves comprise the *pistil.* Inside this pistil are the special spore cases called *ovules.* Each ovule produces one spore which grows into a female plant without ever leaving the ovule, so that each ripe ovule contains eight cells, one of which is an egg. Surrounding the pistil is a ring of differently specialized leaves, the *stamens.* At the top of each stamen is a spore case, in which many tiny spores are produced. These spores are called "pollen grains," and they germinate to produce male plants, as we shall see. The spore-bearing leaves are surrounded by a ring of brightly colored and sweet-smelling *petals,* and these in turn by the green *sepals.*

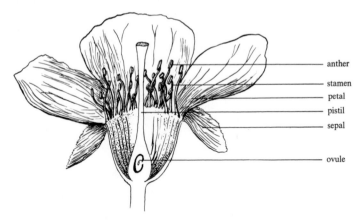

anther

stamen

petal

pistil

sepal

ovule

FIGURE 3-12. A cherry blossom cut in halves.

If a pollen grain is put in a sugar solution, it will germinate into a male plant called a *pollen tube.* This does not

look like much; in fact, it is only a tiny thread containing
three nuclei. In nature, the pollen grain must find its way to
the top of the pistil, and the pollen tube grows down through
the pistil into the ovule, as shown in Figure 3-13. Here one
of its nuclei fertilizes the egg. The process differs from the reproduction of *Selaginella* in two important ways: the male-
forming spores are transported to the vicinity of the egg
before they germinate, so that sperms do not have to swim
through water; and the zygote does not immediately leave
its parent plant. Instead, it grows into a large embryo, ac-
cumulates some stored food, and forms a thick protective
coat. It becomes a *seed*.

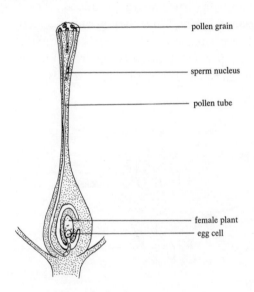

FIGURE 3-13. Fertilization of the egg in a cherry blossom.

Flowering plants can live in dry climates, even in deserts. They do not even need dew for their sperms to swim
through, because the pollen grain is transported. The zygote

does not need favorable conditions immediately, for it is protected in a seed. The occasional brief rainy spells in deserts are followed by the germination of thousands of seeds that lie dormant in the soil, in readiness for the short period every few years in which they can grow. The pollen grain and the seed freed plants from life in the water, but they involve new problems. The pollen grain must somehow get to the pistil. If possible, it should be the pistil of a different plant in order to maintain the variation of the species. And the seed must be carried away from its parent plant to colonize new areas.

The earliest flowering plants relied on the wind to carry their pollen from place to place, and many still do. Corn, grasses, oak trees, and others release enormous amounts of pollen into the air. Flowers that are pollinated by wind need no petals and have none, but the upper end of the pistil is formed into a broad, feathery structure that traps pollen efficiently. Wind pollination works well if two conditions are met: the pollen must be produced in large quantity; and the plants must grow in large stands, so that no plant is far from others of the same species. The shrinking violet, cowering on the floor of a forest, has little chance of receiving pollen from another if it relies on the wind and its nearest prospective mate is several yards away.

Flowers with sweet smell and brightly colored petals are not pollinated by the wind. Their pollen is transferred by insects. The petals of a clover flower secrete a sweet, sugary liquid that serves as food for the bees. In traveling from flower to flower, the bees become covered with pollen and distribute it as they go. Insects have special tastes in nectar and are likely to confine their visits to a single species of flower, so that they rarely transfer pollen to the wrong species. The bright colors and sweet smell enable the cruising insect to find the flower that tickles his particular palate, so even isolated flowers do not go unpollinated.

Some of the special adaptations between flower and insect border on the fantastic. The yucca, or Spanish bayonet, a plant of our arid southwest, is pollinated only by a certain moth. The female moth lays its eggs in the pistil, then climbs to the top of the pistil and deposits a load of pollen. Before leaving, the moth gathers more pollen and passes on to the next plant. The flower is thus cross-pollinated, and a few of the seeds formed serve as food for the developing moth larva. In South America Charles Darwin found an orchid with a lower lip twelve inches long, enclosing two stamens curving gracefully down to allow the spore cases to hang over the opening of the lip. He predicted that there must be a butterfly in the area with a tongue twelve inches long, so that it could sit on the lip and reach the nectar at the bottom, while receiving the spore cases on the top of its head. Such a butterfly was later found. Perhaps the most bizarre case is another South American orchid, whose flowers imitate the body form and coloration of a certain female beetle. The poor, frustrated male beetle pollinates the flowers by attempting to mate with them, one after the other!

Once pollination is completed, the zygote grows into an embryo enclosed in a seed. The seed must have some method of dispersal; that is, some way must be found to transport the seed some distance from its parent. Plants are not motile, and this is the only way that they can spread to new areas. This is the function of fruit, which is the matured wall of the pistil after the stamens, petals, and sepals have fallen away. Sweet, succulent fruits are eaten by animals, who will drop the seed somewhere else. When seeds are small, as a blackberry's, they are eaten, but cannot be digested because they are protected by a waxy coating, and they are deposited in the excreta of the birds that eat the berries. Acorns and other nuts are merely large, nutritious seeds. They depend for their dispersal on the thrifty habits of squirrels and chipmunks, which store nuts for a rainy day. Because of either the limited memory or the short life of these animals, many nuts are never claimed and germinate to replace trees that die.

Not all fruits are edible, and they have developed a variety of mechanisms that disperse the seed. The barbed bristles of burs cling to the fur of passing animals. The wings of a maple key or the feathery parachute of a dandelion seed catch the wind and can carry the seed for miles. A witch hazel fruit explodes while still attached to the tree, propelling its shiny, streamlined seeds twenty feet or more. Coconut trees grow on all tropical beaches of the world, for their nuts fall from the trees enclosed in a thick, leathery shell surrounding a spongy, air-filled material that enables them to float across miles of ocean. By one means or another, each seed is dispersed by the fruit that encases it.

DEGENERATION OF THE SEXUAL PROCESS

No conscience leads evolution into the best path; no inner voice issues dire warnings when a species begins to neglect sexual methods in favor of the more convenient asexual methods of reproduction. Because of the short-range benefits of the more efficient asexual processes, many species have lost their sexual processes to some degree. A banana tree is the most outrageous example. It reproduces asexually by means of runners; but it also forms flowers that attract hummingbirds which cross-pollinate the flowers. Fertilization of the eggs is followed by the growth of great bunches of succulent fruit, a storehouse of quantities of food produced in the leaves. And the fruit contains no seeds! Year after year, banana plants go through the motions of sexual reproduction and then fail to complete the process. They are maintained by asexual means only.

Many plants and some animals as well have retreated from basic sexual reproduction in ways not nearly so drastic. The garden pea forms a colorful, sweet-smelling flower—which never opens! The flower advertises, but when the customer comes, the door is closed and the flowers pollinate themselves. This is not unusual; wheat, in a normally wind-pollinated family, never opens its flowers to the breeze. The sexual process is not completely useless, for there is still some recombination of chromosomes, but failure of the chromosomes to recombine on a population-wide basis leads to considerable uniformity. Self-fertilizing animals have gone the same way—some snails, sea-walnuts, many parasitic worms, and barnacles normally possess both sets of sex organs and fertilize themselves.

The philosopher Friedrich Engels once used this process to make the point that morality consists of much more than socially approved sexual behavior. He said, "If strict monogamy is the sole criterion of virtue, then the palm must go to the tapeworm, which carries a complete male and female sexual apparatus in each of its fifty to two hundred body segments and passes its whole lifetime in fertilizing itself in every one of these segments."

Parthenogenesis is a still more extreme loss of the sexual process, essentially a retreat to complete asexuality. Parthenogenesis is the process by which certain rotifers, "water fleas," insects, and flatworms produce eggs that develop into female larvae without fertilization. In some species, no males are known at all. Parthenogenesis is sometimes one phase of a kind of alternation of generations, as in aphids that attack rosebushes; several parthenogenetic generations are produced throughout the summer, but eggs are fertilized in the fall and the zygotes survive over the winter.

In many flowering plants, seed is formed without fertilization of the egg.

If the world never changed, creatures with degenerate sexual processes or with none at all would stand a better chance of survival than sexual organisms, for they reproduce more efficiently. This is undoubtedly why the sexual process degenerates. But when conditions change, it is more often the sexual creatures that survive the crisis.

4

‧‧‧‧‧‧‧‧‧‧‧‧‧‧‧‧‧‧‧‧‧‧‧‧‧‧‧‧‧‧‧‧‧‧‧‧‧‧

Hormones and
Sex Behavior

Higher animals have much more efficient reproductive methods than lower animals and plants. To keep the population size more or less constant, starfishes must lay a million eggs at a time, for most are eaten before they grow up. A robin lays four eggs and then watches over them, incubates them, and feeds the young for a while after they hatch. Greater efficiency has been achieved by complicating the business of raising a family. Not only the physical structure of the robin, but also its behavior are crucial to the job of robin-rearing. In recent years, much has been learned about mechanisms that control and co-ordinate the physical and behavioral aspects of the reproductive mechanism in animals. And every investigation has led to hormones.

From an experimental viewpoint, it started in 1889, when the famous French physiologist Charles Brown-Sequard announced that he had succeeded in rejuvenating himself. He was then seventy-two years old and had gained the great respect of his fellow scientists by his work on the physiology of the nervous system. In his later years, he interested himself in work that had been done on transplantations of the testis of the fowl and soon announced that it had led to a way to make an old man young.

THE DISCOVERY OF HORMONES

It has been common knowledge for hundreds of years that an animal or man deprived of his testes develops quite differently from normally endowed males of his species. In general, the bodily changes that normally accompany growing up simply do not occur. Castrated boys remain infantile for life: they never grow hair on the face or body or lose it on the head, their penes and other sex organs do not grow, their voices do not change, they form no sex drive. There is a tendency for the muscles to be flabby and for fat to accumulate. Until the nineteenth century, it was customary for choirs to obtain high voices by castration of boys, since women were not permitted to sing in public. Castration of animals (spaying of cats or dogs, gelding of horses, caponizing of roosters) has been practiced for centuries to produce docility (in horses, oxen, and dogs) or tender meat (in steers and capons).

But no one knew what the connection was between the testes and other organs of the body. It was known that every organ of the body had to have its activity co-ordinated with all other parts, and that co-ordination was the function of the nervous system. From the brain, nerves connect to each muscle fiber, gland, and center of sensation. Much of this mass of telephone cable-like nerves is routed through the spinal cord. When you take a single step, thousands of impulses from your skin, muscles, eyes, ears, and semicircular canals inform your brain of what is happening at each moment of the process. The brain and spinal cord digest all this information as it arrives and send impulses to the muscles of your legs, trunk, arms, and neck that perform the actual motion. In a similar way, every part of your body—hands, heart, stomach, salivary glands, eyes, sex organs—is controlled by nervous impulses.

All physiologists expected to find nervous connections to the testes that would explain the peculiar control they exert over the masculinization of the body. Some years before Brown-Sequard's dramatic announcement, an important experiment was done with a fowl that had been castrated at an early age. Normally, it would grow into a capon—fat, docile, sexless, without the stately bearing, the wattles, and comb of a rooster. In this case, a testis from another rooster was implanted into the abdomen of the capon, and the bird developed its normal male sexual characteristics. It did not matter where the testis was placed, so it seemed impossible that the effect was due to nervous connections. It was suggested that the testis secretes something into the blood, which then carries it throughout the body to produce its effects on different organs.

Brown-Sequard made an extract of the testes of a bull and injected it into himself. The results were miraculous. He developed a spring in his step, greater endurance, the psychological outlook of a vigorous, young man, and a restoration of sexual potency that had waned with advancing age. The world was astonished, and for several decades, testis extracts and transplants were put into aging men. "Monkey glands" and "goat glands" became household words and the subject of innumerable jokes, but they were also taken seriously. The effect was ascribed to a substance elaborated by the testis and released into the blood—a *hormone*.

It is sad to conclude the story, for Brown-Sequard soon recovered from abnormal youthfulness and began once again to act his age. Ten men in a home for the aged were given the hormone injections by the doctor in charge, and all ten were rejuvenated as expected. But the doctor found that he got the same results with ten other men—using salt water instead of testis extract! It became clear that the rejuvenation Brown-Sequard offered to a delighted humanity was the result of self-delusion. Surely there is no yearning stronger than that of an old man to regain his youth. If you persuade him that you can help him do this, his own desires will do the rest, making him believe and act, for a while at least, as though the treatment were successful. The whole incident of the monkey glands, farcical as it was, had two important results: it made clear the importance of controls in medical experimentation, and it made people conscious of the existence of those elusive substances, the hormones.

The first unquestionable demonstration that hormones exist came in 1904 and had nothing to do with sex. After you have eaten a meal, the food passes slowly out of your stomach into your small intestine. At the same time, the pancreas secretes a digestive juice that flows through a duct into the small intestine, where it mixes with the food. It was found that the flow of pancreatic juice could be stimulated by putting acid in the small intestine, simulating the natural acid of the stomach juice. There were many searches for the nervous connection that sensed the acid in the small intestine and sent a signal to the pancreas, but none was ever found. In one experiment, all the nervous connections to the small intestine of a dog were severed and a tube inserted into the pancreatic duct to catch the juice. After the dog recovered from the operation, it was still able to produce the response. Perhaps some of the stomach acid got into the blood and finally reached the pancreas. Injections of acid into the blood produced no result.

Finally it was suggested that the information was carried by a hormone secreted by the small intestine in response to the arrival of acid from the stomach, and serving to stimulate secretion by the pancreas. This was tested by many ingenious experiments. For instance, acid was placed in the intestine of a dog, which was then killed; an extract of its intestinal lining caused the pancreas of another dog to secrete, just as if it were busily digesting a meal. In another experiment, two dogs were united by their arteries so that the same blood flowed through both; acid in the intestine of either dog produced pancreatic secretion in both. Another time, an isolated piece of intestine and a pancreas were separately transplanted from one dog to another; stimulation of the transplanted intestine caused secretion by both the transplanted and the natural pancreas. The hormone that the intestine produces has been isolated in pure form and is now known as *secretin*.

Since the discovery of secretin, over forty hormones have been found in the human body. They are produced in the intestine, stomach, pancreas, brain, testes, ovaries, kidneys, liver, adrenal glands, pituitary gland, thyroid gland, and probably other organs. It is likely that the number of hormones as yet undiscovered is greater than the number we already know. Chemically, they are proteins, steroids, amino acids, and peptides. Most produce effects in many parts of the body and nearly all affect the sex functions in one way or another.

SEX HORMONES

Although most hormones are involved in the sex and reproductive functions, some seem to have as their primary responsibility the control of these functions. In the human body, there are, so far as we know, nine sex hormones. Most are found in many other animals as well, although often in slightly different form. We will briefly note the physiological effects produced by each of these sex hormones and then turn our attention to the question of how they affect the sex behavior of animals.

Testosterone This is the male hormone whose existence was deduced by Brown-Sequard with such disastrous results. It is produced by the testes and is responsible (in man) for those changes that turn a boy into a man—deepening of the voice, growth of the sex organs, growth of hair on the face and body, loss of hair on the head, and sex drive. It has corresponding functions in other animals; in the rooster, for example, it causes growth of the comb and wattles, aggressiveness, and sexual behavior.

Studying the effects of a single hormone on the body is something like trying to understand a game of chess by observing the moves of one piece. The above outline of the effects of testosterone is adequate for our purposes, but the picture is complicated by at least seven factors. First, several chemicals may have identical effects, more or less strongly, and more than one may be in the blood simultaneously. Second, the hormones may be produced in different parts of the body; testosterone, or something like it, is made in the ovaries of a woman as well as the testes of a man. A male hormone is also made in the adrenal gland, and an adrenal tumor in a woman produces the bearded lady of the circus.

Third, the presence of a hormone in the blood may either stimulate or inhibit other glands in hormone production; a hormone of the pituitary gland stimulates the testis to make testosterone. Fourth, two quite different hormones may produce similar effects; axillary and pubic hair growth is stimulated by both male and female hormones. Fifth, it may take more than one hormone to produce a given effect; testosterone does its work well only in the presence of hormones from the adrenal and thyroid glands.

Sixth, we only mention the most obvious effects of the hormones; actually, nearly every tissue in the body changes during adolescence as a response to the presence of testosterone. And finally, the effect of the hormone may vary according to the age of the individual; a month before a boy is born, his testes produce testosterone for a short period, and the only effect seems to be the descent of the testes from their original position in the abdomen into the scrotum.

Bear in mind, then, that the brief outlines given below of the effects of various hormones would have to be hedged with enough qualifications, interactions, and exceptions to fill a large book (there are many such in existence) if we wanted to do a thorough job. Let us be content with a brief description of the activity of the remaining eight sex hormones.

Estrogen This is the female hormone, produced in the ovaries by the follicles that also form egg cells. Like testosterone, it is not made in childhood, but causes the changes of adolescence. It stimulates the deposition of fat in the skin, particularly in the breasts and hips, giving mature women their rounded outlines. It causes axillary and pubic hair to grow. The secondary sex organs—vagina, uterus, external genitals, ducts of the breasts (but not the glandular tissue)—change to their mature forms. Like the male hormone, it causes the development of sexual feelings. There is no evidence that either the male or the female hormone has any effect on the *direction* of these desires, and it is certain that homosexual feelings have nothing to do with hormones. Finally, the female hormone causes an egg to mature in the ovary.

Progesterone The maturing of an egg starts off a chain of reactions that prepares the female body for pregnancy, and the crucial role in this series is played by progesterone.

When an egg is fully mature, the follicle bursts, forcing the egg out into the fallopian tube where it can be fertilized (Figure 4-1). The empty follicle now grows into a special gland (the *corpus luteum,* or yellow body) that produces progesterone. This hormone, together with estrogen, acts on the wall of the uterus, which has already thickened somewhat due to the effects of the same estrogen that caused the follicle to ripen. When progesterone comes on the scene, the wall becomes very thick and forms a rich blood supply and a complex set of mucus glands, so that the fertilized egg has a nest ready for it when it reaches the uterus.

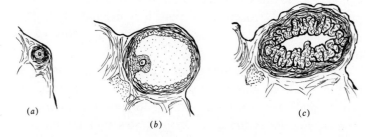

(a)

(b)

(c)

FIGURE 4-1. History of a follicle: (*a*) unripe egg in follicle; (*b*) ripe egg; (*c*) corpus luteum.

Throughout pregnancy, these two hormones are necessary for the continued growth of the muscles and lining of the uterus, and if for any reason the hormone supply is cut off, the embryo will be cast out. Both female hormones are supplied by the corpus luteum for about four months, and then the placenta of the embryo takes over the job.

The second effect of progesterone is on the breasts. Estrogen produces growth of the milk ducts, but progesterone is needed to cause formation of the tiny glands at the ends of these ducts where milk is produced. This is why breasts are ready to make milk when the baby is born.

Most human eggs, of course, are not fertilized. Then the corpus luteum continues to make its hormones for only about ten days. When it stops, the lining of the uterus breaks down, with considerable bleeding, a process called "menstruation." A new follicle now begins to grow in the ovary. It starts to make estrogen, which stimulates new growth of the uterus wall, and the whole cycle repeats itself.

Follicle-Stimulating Hormone (FSH) The pea-sized pituitary gland, hanging on a stalk below the base of the brain, makes a number of hormones, several of which are directly connected with the reproductive functions. FSH stimulates the growth of the egg follicle in a woman and the production of estrogen. In a man, it is needed for maintenance and repair of the sperm-making apparatus of the testes.

Luteinizing Hormone (LH) This hormone, also made by the pituitary gland, causes the release of the egg and growth and secretion by the corpus luteum in a woman. In men, it stimulates the cells of the testes that produce testosterone.

Prolactin This is another pituitary hormone, secreted during and especially after pregnancy. After estrogen has caused the milk ducts to grow and progesterone has made the glands form, prolactin stimulates these glands to make milk. If this milk is drained out of the breasts, as by a sucking infant, prolactin production continues so that more milk is produced. When the nipple is no longer stimulated by the sucking infant, the production of prolactin stops and the breasts revert to their former condition. Prolactin is also needed for normal functioning of the corpus luteum. Human prolactin now seems to be identical with human growth hormone, the pituitary material that stimulates the general growth of the body. It is not the same as the growth hormones of animal origin.*

These last five hormones control the menstrual cycle of a woman and provide us with a fine example of the way hormones interact with each other. FSH from the pituitary gland causes the growth of a follicle. The follicle produces estrogen, which causes the growth of the uterus wall. But this estrogen also affects the pituitary gland (indirectly, by way of part of the brain). As the estrogen in the blood builds up, the pituitary responds by making less FSH and more LH and prolactin. This results in expulsion of the egg from the follicle and growth of the corpus luteum. For the next ten days, progesterone is produced by the corpus luteum, causing further preparation of the uterus. Then the corpus luteum degenerates, so that the supplies of both estrogen and progesterone are cut off. This has two effects: menstruation, and increase in FSH production by the pituitary gland, which starts the whole cycle again.

Human Chorionic Gonadotropin (HCG) The menstrual cycle must be interrupted when a woman becomes pregnant. This means that the corpus luteum, instead of degenerating after ten days, must continue to produce its hormones to maintain the wall and muscles of the uterus for several months, until the placenta of the embryo can take over the job. The interruption is caused by HCG, which is produced by the membranes that surround the developing embryo. Shortly after the embryo is implanted in the uterus

---

*As this book goes to press, discovery of a hormone (or hormones) with the activity of both prolactin and growth hormone, produced in the human placenta, has been announced. So far, it has not been purified, so we do not know whether it is identical with pituitary prolactin. We can only guess its function: perhaps it is needed to stimulate growth of the embryo.

wall, it begins to make HCG. This hormone prevents the collapse of the corpus luteum. For the first six weeks of pregnancy, large amounts of HCG are released by the embryo into its mother's bloodstream, and the amount diminishes as the placenta takes over the production of estrogen and progesterone, as well as the newly discovered prolactin-like material.

Relaxin This recently discovered hormone is secreted during pregnancy by the ovary. It prepares the mother for giving birth by causing the cervix (the muscular ring that separates the uterus from the vagina) to become soft and by relaxing the ligaments that hold the pelvic bones. Thus it allows the birth canal to open so that the baby can pass out.

Oxytocin Two separate functions are known for this pituitary hormone. It has a general effect on the smooth muscles of the body, particularly on the muscles of the uterus. It is produced in large amounts during labor, and is partly responsible for the uterine contractions that expel the baby. This is the material that a doctor injects when he wants to "induce labor"; that is, to cause the baby to be born.

Oxytocin is the last of the four hormones needed for milk production, for it causes the "let-down reflex," the actual flow of milk. When the breast has been properly prepared by estrogen, progesterone, and prolactin, the stimulation of the mother's nipple by the baby starts nerve impulses going to the brain, where they influence the pituitary gland. The pituitary releases oxytocin, which gets to the milk glands and starts the milk flowing. Oxytocin production is controlled by the nervous system; it is a reflex and can be conditioned. A nursing mother may start flowing at the breast just from hearing her baby cry in the middle of the night.

This is only a small part of what sex hormones do. I have described above only their most obvious effects. Practically any process can be affected by any of a long list of hormones.

SECONDARY SEX CHARACTERISTICS

When the early spring flowers peep up through the rapidly melting snow of our northern forests, two bony knobs appear on the head of the adult male deer. Stimulated by pituitary secretions, these will soon grow into the spreading antlers that give the buck his aristocratic appearance. With the approach of mating season in late summer, male hormone pours into the blood from the testes, causing the antlers to harden and shed their velvety covering. These antlers are an essential part of a deer's mating equipment, for they are used in the battle between males that always precedes mating. Several females watch the fight. The battle stimulates both the struggling males and the female audience sexually, and the victorious buck has a harem at his disposal. When the end of the mating season brings a waning of the activity of the testes, the antlers drop off.

Perhaps you find it difficult to imagine why the sight of two bucks rushing at each other antlers first is sexually exciting, but that is only because you are not a doe. Psychological readiness for mating is produced by different stimuli for every species. A female moth ready for mating emits an odor that attracts every male within a half mile, just as a female dog in heat brings all the neighborhood males to her in a sexually excited state. This is quite general among mammals, most of which depend strongly on their noses for information about their world, including the location of females. The voice of the opposite sex is a powerful sexual stimulant in many species, including the spring peepers whose whistles are heard in the swamps, the croaking bullfrogs, the trumpeting elephant, and the cats that sometimes make spring nights hideous. Quite commonly one sex or the other has some distinctive feature, often brightly colored, that is displayed to produce arousal in a prospective mate. The male man-of-war bird woos his mate with an inflatable, red air sac below his chin, and a female guppy becomes ready for mating when she sees the bright scales of the male.

Sometimes the female has the bright display colors; when a female chimpanzee is fertile and receptive, her genitals are surrounded by a bright red patch of bare skin, which she displays to available males. There is no subtlety about this advertisement for a mate, but it is remarkably effective, for it greatly excites the male. Often it is only the behavior of an animal that conveys its readiness to mate; a male English sparrow stimulates the female by repeatedly crouching before her and fluttering his wings.

Among vertebrates, sexual intercourse is almost always preceded by courtship. Mating is seasonal. At a particular time of year, the female has ripe eggs in her ovaries, and both sexes are ready for mating. The secondary sex characteristics—the antlers of a deer, the sex skin of a female ape, the inflatable sacs of many frogs and certain birds, the bright colors of a variety of creatures—have reached their greatest development. The sex organs are also ready. In creatures such as ducks and mice, the penis grows to usable size. In ground squirrels, cats, and other mammals the testes descend out of the abdomen into the scrotum, where the cooler temperature favors the formation of active sperms. When all is ready, the two individuals stimulate each other by a combination of smells, calls, color displays, and provocative actions until both have reached a peak of excitement, and then intercourse occurs.

Courting behavior is different for each species. It may involve fighting between males while the females watch (deer, seals, wild sheep), special dances or patterns of flight (most birds), or display of bright colors (many lizards and birds), but each animal will become aroused only by the characteristic behavior of the opposite sex of the same species.

If any generalization in endocrinology is valid, it is this one: secondary sex organs, that is, all organs that are different in the two sexes except the gamete-producing glands, develop in response to secretions of the ovaries or testes, and the kind of organs that grow depends on which kind of primary sex organ is doing the secreting. Testosterone will grow hair on a woman's face, a comb on a hen, masculine coloring in a female guppy, or a long, pointed tail fin on a female swordtail. It will produce the changes in the male of any species that will bring it into full breeding condition at any time of the year.

Estrogen will produce swelling of the sex skin of an ape, grow breasts on a man, or produce long, fluffy, "henny" feathers in a rooster. In every species of vertebrate that has been tested experimentally, these two hormones give the individual nearly every aspect of maleness or femaleness. Since these hormones prepare both the courtship and mating apparatus and the reproductive organs, intercourse occurs only when fertilization of eggs is possible and is nearly always followed by production of a new generation.

Actions and behavior are controlled directly by the nervous system. The brain receives impulses from the sense organs and sends out instructions by way of the spinal cord and nerves to the muscles that move the body. But hormones also affect behavior. Frogs and lizards, roosters and pigeons, mice, monkeys, dogs, and men have all been induced to go through complete courtship and mating even though they had been castrated when very young, by administration of testosterone. Sex hormones not only bring the reproductive organs into functional condition, but produce the behavior patterns that bring about reproduction. In a recent experiment, just enough estrogen to wet the end of a needle was injected into the hypothalamus at the base of the brain of a female cat. The result was spectacular. In spite of the fact that the animal was not in mating condition, she went through all the actions of a cat in heat, and succeeded in attracting and mating with a male.

Hormones can make changes in behavior even when they produce no visible physical changes. A male dog castrated when young will urinate like a puppy or a female throughout its life, in a squatting position. Administration of testosterone will cause it to change its posture and raise its hind leg to urinate, like any self-respecting male. This seems to be some direct effect on the nervous system, although it is impossible to rule out experimentally the possibility that the primary effect of the hormone is on some specific organ.

HORMONES AND MATING

In temperate climates, it is important that mating occur at the proper time of year. If fawns were born in November, they would be too young to survive the rigors of winter. By what mechanism does the nervous-hormonal system of an animal control the time of mating so as to give the young their best chance of growing up? In most cases, the stimulus seems to be the changing length of the day as the seasons change. Birds and many mammals can be brought into breeding condition at any time of the year in the laboratory by the simple expedient of increasing the period in which their cages are illuminated each day. Mares, which ordinarily come into heat in the spring, can be caused to breed in August or September by removing them to the Southern hemisphere, where the seasons are reversed. Brook trout can be made to breed in December, merely by manipulation of the light.

The mechanism by which this remarkable control is exerted has been extensively investigated, and is fairly well understood, at least among certain birds. With the coming of spring, the increase in the length of daylight hours produces changes in a tiny section of the base of the brain known as the *hypothalamus*. This is the control center for the pituitary gland, which hangs just below the hypothalamus on a little stalk. Two tiny blood vessels carry blood from the hypothalamus into the pituitary gland. Although no one has yet succeeded in isolating the chemicals involved, there is ample evidence that the hypothalamus gives instructions to the pituitary gland by secreting minute quantities of special substances into these vessels. These can cause the pituitary gland to secrete follicle-stimulating hormone into the general circulation. When this FSH arrives at the ovaries or testes, the primary sex organ responds by secreting estrogen or testosterone, depending on the sex of the individual.

Thus, as the days grow longer, the sex hormones pour into the blood, causing the growth of ovaries or testes and other secondary sex organs. This in turn acts back on the nervous system and results in the mating calls of frogs, the fighting of deer, the brazen invitation of chimpanzees, the wing-fluttering of sparrows, and all the rigmarole that these creatures must go through to obtain a mate and produce a new generation.

The hypothalamus is part of the brain and can receive nervous impulses from any part of the body through the millions of telephone wires that co-ordinate all the activity of the animal. A mink-rancher may know nothing about hormones, but he does know that he can bring the females into heat earlier in the year by putting a male in the next cage. The sensory stimulation of a nearby male excites the female and starts the hypothalamus secretions earlier than they would otherwise occur. When a cat or a rabbit is in heat, its ovaries hold their eggs. The excitement of intercourse produces a general nervous stimulation, and the brain sends nerve messages to the hypothalamus. From here secretions pass to the pituitary, which responds by secreting luteinizing hormone. The LH travels through the general circulation until it arrives at the ovaries and causes the eggs to be released, so that they can be fertilized by the recently injected sperms. The link between the hypothalamus and the pituitary is the main one by which the nervous system exerts its control over the sex hormones.

With this background, perhaps we can understand the mechanism that controls the breeding cycle of birds. This cycle takes many forms, but the description given below is fairly typical of migratory songbirds. As the day lengthens in spring, the growth of the testes or ovaries is accompanied by a restlessness which culminates in a long migratory flight from winter quarters to the nesting grounds further north. When the male arrives, he carves out a suitable territory by flying from one branch to another, singing on each perch again and again to warn off other males of the same species. Sometimes there is actual fighting, but as a rule the most aggressive male will win a particular bush by threats, bluster, and bluff. He then admits a female to his territory and starts to court her by displaying bright colors, by assuming provocative postures, by chasing her through the territory in frantic flights.

All this courtship activity, which may continue for days or weeks, stimulates both the male and the female, and the vital juices begin to flow from the hypothalamus to the pituitary, stimulating the pituitary to release its hormones into the blood. When these get to the sex organ, they cause a release of the sex hormones into the general circulation. As the estrogen content of the blood of the female increases, she becomes sexually receptive and the eggs grow in her ovaries. During this period, she will allow the male to mount her several times a day, and will also start building her nest. It is clear that both these activities are the result of the hormone secreted by her ovaries, for she will mate and build a nest with no courtship at all if estrogen is injected. The role of courtship seems to be to stimulate her pituitary to secrete FSH.

When the nest is complete, an egg is released from the ovary and is immediately fertilized by the sperms that have been in the oviduct for several days, all during the nest-building phase. As the eggs pass down the oviduct, glands in the wall of this tube deposit a thick layer of albumen, then a membrane, then the shell, and finally the pigment that colors the shell. At the end of a day, the egg is laid and another is released to start its trip down the oviduct.

The whole procedure is under control of hormones, starting with the FSH that causes the ovaries to work. When an egg becomes fully mature, the ovary releases progesterone. This hormone, which, you remember, prepares the uterus for pregnancy in mammals, is what causes the oviducts of the bird to produce their secretions. It also causes the pituitary to release LH (possibly by way of the effect on the hypothalamus), which causes the egg to be released from the ovary into the well-prepared oviduct. As the egg passes down the oviduct, it stimulates the oviduct mechanically, starting nervous signals that reach the brain and are transmitted to the pituitary as orders to *stop* making LH. Therefore, the second egg is not released until the first one is laid and the oviduct no longer receives its stimulation.

Egg production is a carefully controlled process. A bird normally lays an egg every day until a full clutch has been laid and then stops. It does not release one from the ovary until about an hour after the previous one has been laid; it will stop laying altogether if its nest is removed. Some birds will continue to lay an egg every day if one is removed every day, and a flicker can be made to lay forty or fifty eggs by this method. Egg production can obviously be stopped by sensory stimuli: an egg in the oviduct, a full clutch in the nest, or absence of the nest. It is reasonably certain that these stimuli act by way of the brain-hypothalamus-pituitary link to stop the production of LH and thereby stop the release of eggs from the ovary.

Hormones and the Care of the Young

Birds are not finished with reproductive duties when they have laid their eggs. If their reproductive efforts are to be fruitful, the birds must sit on the eggs to keep them warm until they hatch, and then they must keep their young warm in the same way for a few days. They must feed their young and clean their nests until their offspring can fend for themselves. Mammals carry their eggs around inside until they "hatch" and so do not have to incubate; but they must suckle their young and protect them until they are weaned. Much nonsense has been written about "mother love" and "maternal instinct" in describing such behavior. A mother sheep will protect her lamb, retrieve it if it strays, wash it with her tongue, and suckle it for many weeks. If you are sentimental enough for this to bring a lump to your throat and a suspicion of moisture to your eye, suppress it, for if you wash the lamb as soon as it is born, the mother lamb will want nothing to do with it. A cat would probably eat her kitten.

Does a bird sit on its eggs to keep them warm so that she can raise a family that will make her proud and happy? She will sit just as happily on a golf ball. In fact, she will sit far longer on a golf ball, for it does not hatch. A bird never seems to be upset if the egg does not hatch; on the contrary, she is probably surprised when it does. She sits on the eggs and cares for her young only because her body is in a particular physiological condition, because she has internal stresses that can be relieved by maternal behavior.

One of the best examples of maternal behavior relieving stress occurs in pigeons and doves. Their young are fed for their first few days on a cheesy mass of cells cast off from a part of the digestive system—the crop—in the throat of the parents. When a ring dove incubates, the crop milk forms so that food is available to the young as soon as they hatch. If the bird is new at parenthood, she does not at first know how to get rid of this accumulation of crop milk. She makes retching movements, as though she felt nauseated and could not regurgitate. Sooner or later, the bird touches the head of its newly hatched squabs, and the young bird responds by stroking the mother's throat with its bill. This provides the stimulus for regurgitating the crop milk, which flows into the mouths of the hungry squabs. Ring doves who have bred before will go to the young almost as soon as they hatch to relieve themselves of the irritating material in their crops.

If the crop is anesthetized so that the bird cannot feel discomfort when its crop is full of crop milk, it will make no effort to feed its young. Similarly, a cow is uncomfortable when full of milk and finds relief by suckling its calf. But a milking machine will content it just as much. Mother love indeed!

Whatever it is that makes animals care for their young, it is not the lofty sentiments that motivated your parents to raise you. Animals act in an automatic way. Each stimulus from the environment supplies information, cues to tell the creatures how to act. The way the organism responds depends only on what kind of animal it is and on its physiological condition at the time. Love and hate, reason and emotion have practically nothing to do with behavior. In the normal course of events, the stimuli come in a certain order and the body responds in the appropriate way to produce the behavior necessary to complete the life cycle. If the environment is altered—for instance, by removing the odor from a newborn kitten by washing—or if the internal conditions are changed—by injecting the wrong hormone—the animal's behavior becomes inappropriate, and the breeding cycle will probably be interrupted.

The internal environment, the physiological condition of the animal, is controlled by its secretion of hormones. The breeding cycle of a female bird or mammal passes through three phases, each dominated by a different hormone. During the nonbreeding season, there is little ovarian activity. Then the coming of the breeding season and the courtship of the male bring the female into the sexual phase, due to the secretion of estrogen. Secondary sex characteristics develop, eggs begin to grow in the ovary, there may be nest-building, and sexual intercourse occurs. With the release of the egg into the oviduct, the animal becomes more and more dominated by progesterone from her corpus luteum and passes into the reproductive phase. In birds, this means secretion of egg coatings by the oviduct and laying and incubating the eggs; in mammals it means pregnancy. Once eggs are laid or young are born, the animal passes into a maternal phase, dominated by prolactin, when the young are protected and fed. This picture is oversimplified and varies from one species to another, but it is a broad outline on which to base further discussion.

Any one phase must prepare the animal for the next. During the nest-building, sexual phase of a female bird's cycle, when her functioning is dominated by estrogen, her lower abdomen becomes swollen with large numbers of sub-surface blood vessels. This can be brought on at any time by estrogen injections. Her body is preparing for the later, reproductive phase, for this is the beginning of the *incubation patch,* the region of bare, inflamed skin that warms the eggs. In mammals, the uterus and breasts develop in response to estrogen during the sexual phase, again a preparation for reproductive functions.

As we have seen above, release of eggs is followed by secretion of progesterone from the ovary along with estrogen, ushering in the reproductive phase. In mammals, this produces the changes needed for pregnancy; in birds, it causes secretion of materials that complete the egg as it passes down the oviduct. For some reason, it also causes birds to sit on their eggs. A ring dove treated with progesterone for seven days will incubate almost immediately if it is put into a cage containing a nest and eggs, even if it has not gone through any of the previous stages.

In mammals, production of prolactin, which comes from the pituitary gland, increases greatly with the birth of the young, possibly due to cessation of progesterone production of the placenta. In birds, on the other hand, secretion of prolactin builds up gradually during the entire incubation period when the egg is turning into a bird. Prolactin causes formation of milk in the breasts and of crop milk in pigeons. Most birds, of course, do not produce any form of milk, but prolactin is important nevertheless. It causes the loss of feathers on the incubation patch, exposing naked, hot skin to be placed next to the eggs. Birds do not give birth, of course, and it has been suggested that the stimulus for prolactin production is the act of sitting on the eggs.

The transition from one phase to another is controlled by the pituitary gland. As the breeding season approaches, the FSH produced by this tiny bit of tissue hanging from the bottom of the brain stimulates the ovary to make estrogen. As the sexual phase draws to a close, the pituitary produces LH, causing the ovary to release its egg and bring the body into the reproductive phase by secreting progesterone. When young are born or eggs laid, the pituitary makes prolactin. This hormone, in addition to other effects, ends the activity of the ovary, and reproduction gives way to nurturing.

Birds do not sit on eggs in order to produce a family. Then why do they sit? It has been suggested that the devotion and self-sacrifice of an incubating bird is nothing more than a convenient way to cool off the incubation patch which has become hot and uncomfortable. There may be some truth to this ice-pack theory, but a penguin could surely find more effective cooling agents if it needed them. Furthermore, many birds have no incubation patch. Experience plays an important part in incubation behavior. A ring dove, which has no patch, will go immediately to a nest and eggs if first treated with proper hormones. But if it has never raised a brood of its own, it takes much longer for the bird to find the eggs, and some will never incubate at all.

Many problems in this area are awaiting investigation. What makes a male bird grow an incubation patch and sit on eggs? How do other hormones (particularly those of the adrenal gland, which are known to be necessary at many stages) enter into reproductive behavior? Do the nerve pathways to the adrenal gland provide a second link between the nervous system and the ductless glands for control of behavior? How does the function of the hormones vary in different species, aside from the half-dozen mammals and the two dozen birds that have been studied? To what extent and in what ways do hormones affect human sex behavior? The hormones have such drastic influences on the physiology and psychology of the organism that there is no guessing where this work will lead.

5

~~~~~~~~~~~~~~~~~~~~~~~~~~~~~~~

Human Reproduction

A Martian biologist once visited Earth to study animal life. Man puzzled him greatly, for he seemed to be built like other animals, but he lived in a different way. He could hold an intelligent conversation, which is normal for a Martian, but unusual for an animal. Everything he did was somehow animal-like and yet different. He ate and digested food, but he sat at a table and used a knife and fork to do it. He looked at the world around him, but was frequently aided by eyeglasses, telescopes, or microscopes. He walked on his feet, but he used only two instead of the usual four, and those two were protected by the hides of other animals.

Our sex and reproductive processes would be just as puzzling to a Martian. The basic phenomena are much like other animals'; but we have transformed them into processes that are essentially human. Like other female animals, a woman produces eggs in her ovaries and releases them into a fallopian tube. Like other male animals, a man produces sperms in his testes, and they can be carried out in a special fluid produced in other glands. We grow up and court each other. If sexual intercourse occurs while a fresh egg is in the fallopian tube, the sperm may swim from the vagina through the uterus and into the tube, where it fertilizes the egg. The egg then passes into the uterus, where it embeds in the uterus wall. The embryo grows there, forming a placenta and umbilical cord to supply itself with food and oxygen from its mother's blood and to dispose of wastes. When it is full grown, contractions of the uterus and abdominal muscles force it out through the vagina. The now useless placenta then disconnects from the uterus wall and follows the baby out of the mother's body.

Now comes the human part: love and marriage, doctors and hospitals, establishing a home and raising a family. All of this is unlike anything in animal life. The details vary from one culture to another and even within a given culture. We will explore this variation later, but first let us look at the biological aspects of human reproduction.

THE START OF PREGNANCY

Pregnancy begins with fertilization and implantation of the egg. This may sound simple, but there are so many requirements for successful pregnancy that the Martian might easily doubt that it would ever work.

On the male side of the question, the man must be sexually mature and producing large numbers of sperms and adequate amounts of *semen,* the fluid in which the sperms are carried. It takes about fifteen years for a boy to mature sexually, far longer than any other animal. Semen is produced a couple of years earlier, but there are few sperms in it at first. Some men never produce enough sperms, for unless there are hundreds of millions of actively swimming sperms, fertilization of the egg is unlikely. A doctor can easily determine a man's fertility by microscopic examination of his semen. There may be many causes for partial sterility, including poor health, bad diet, hormonal deficiencies, emotional disturbance, and failure of the testis to descend from the abdomen—where it is formed—into the scrotum. This usually occurs shortly before a boy is born and can easily be brought about surgically if it has not happened by adolescence. The other causes of sterility can also be treated, and many a man is now a proud father because of a few visits to the doctor's office.

A girl is mature sexually when her ovaries start their regular rhythm of egg production, some time after menstruation starts. The first egg may be produced anywhere from age twelve to eighteen, and full fertility follows within a couple of years. From then until she reaches menopause somewhere between her fortieth and fifty-fifth birthdays, a woman produces an egg about once every twenty-eight days, except during pregnancy. As with men, a few women never become fully fertile without medical help, again often because of poor health. Sometimes the problem is anatomical, such as a fallopian tube that is closed and prevents the penetration of sperms. This may be caused by infectious diseases, such as gonorrhea. In recent years, diagnosis and treatment of sterility in women has made many women happy mothers.

Even in people who are physically normal, conception may be impeded by psychological problems. A few men are unable to have sexual intercourse because of mental disturbance. Women are almost invariably slower to arouse sexually than men, and some unfortunate women never learn the joy and emotional intimacy that can be achieved in sexual intercourse with a well-loved husband. These problems are sometimes the result of being raised in an atmosphere of extreme prudery where sex is considered shameful, where pleasure is a dirty word, and any sign of youthful sex activity is severely punished. These psychological problems have nothing to do with other causes of infertility, for the most virile men and women may be incompletely fertile for other reasons. Psychological problems call for psychological treatment.

In most animals, intercourse occurs only in the few days a year when the female has fertile eggs in her fallopian tubes. Pregnancy nearly always results. People, on the other hand, are sexually active at all times of the year. A woman is fertile, however, only a couple of days every month, for the egg soon dies unless it is fertilized. If our sex lives were as limited as those of animals, there would be little probability of an egg fulfilling its destiny.

Even if sperms enter the uterus when an egg is in the fallopian tube, they must swim several inches to get to the egg. And when they arrive, their troubles are not over, for the egg is surrounded by a mass of cells that it carried with it from the ovary. The sperms must penetrate this barrier. They do this by secreting an enzyme that dissolves the glue holding the cells together. It has long been believed that the reason so many sperms are needed is that they co-operate in breaking down this cellular barrier. But it has recently been observed that a single rabbit sperm can digest a narrow pathway for itself and push its way to the egg surface. We would still like to know what the rest of those sperms do.

After it is fertilized, the egg is propelled down the fallopian tube by the cilia (hair-like structures) that line the tube. The small store of food in the egg is being used up all this time, and unless the egg is embedded in the nourishing wall of the uterus within three days, it is doomed. Pregnancy is established when the egg touches this wall and sticks to its mucus-coated surface. As we have seen, hormones have prepared the wall for the arrival of the egg, and unless this has been done properly, pregnancy will not follow. If the egg embeds, the uterus wall continues to grow and feeds the embryo for nine months; if not, it sloughs off (menstruation) and a new wall begins to grow.

After all this, only pregnancy has been accomplished; the nine months of development and the complicated process of delivering the baby must then follow. The remarkable thing is the perfect co-ordination of these processes in ninety per cent of adult women. Pregnancy is usually easily accomplished, and the great majority of pregnancies are followed in the course of time by the birth of a baby with no complications.

The fertilization of an egg was originally a simple relationship between two cells meeting, more or less by chance, in the open water. Onto this simple button, evolution has sewn a large and ornately embroidered tattersall vest, consisting of special organs of copulation; organs to retain, protect, and feed the young; complex hormone systems; mating behavior; secondary sex organs; and ultimately differentiated clothing and make-up, cosmetics, dates and dances, jealousy, elaborate white dresses and orange blossoms, in-laws, life insurance, sex literature by the carload, wills, and inheritance taxes. Nothing is simple for human beings.

PREGNANCY AND BIRTH

Women sometimes state that they feel like an entirely different person when they are pregnant. Sometimes they like the new person better. Their posture has become awkward, they develop minor discomforts like varicose veins or constipation, their figures look nothing like those of the movie stars who set the fashion in these matters; but they may also experience a sense of tranquility, of accomplishment, and of closeness to their husbands that transcends anything they have ever felt before. For these women, pregnancy is a beautiful experience.

The pregnant woman is somewhat different from her former self almost at the beginning. Each month of her mature life, a woman passes through a kind of incipient pregnancy. The flow of progesterone from her corpus luteum urges her uterus into growth, makes her breasts swell, and suppresses the activity of her ovaries. If the egg is fertilized and embedded, no menstruation occurs to reverse these trends. The uterus lining, instead of falling apart, continues to grow. The breasts continue to change from fatty tissue into glandular tissue, and a thin, watery fluid flows for a while.

As pregnancy proceeds, bodily changes get progressively greater (Figure 5-1). Foremost is enlargement of the uterus (which is a mere four inches long when not performing its function), until it eventually fills most of the abdominal cavity. A woman who watches her diet carefully while pregnant gains about twenty pounds, nearly half of which is the additional weight of the uterus and the fluid in which the embryo floats. It bulges forward and creates the large, round belly that is the most obvious sign of late pregnancy. It pushes up against the diaphragm, sometimes causing shortness of breath. It reduces the capacity of the stomach and intestines. The entire body is reorganized to accommodate its welcome parasite.

Halfway through its intra-uterine life, the baby begins to exercise its muscles, and the mother knows the joyful excitement of feeling her baby kicking, punching, and changing position. Somewhere between two weeks and two hours before delivery, the uterus drops, and the baby's head, cushioned by a small amount of fluid, pushes against the inner opening of the cervix. A new human being is knocking at the door to the world, with its head!

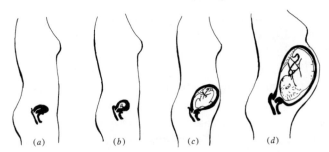

FIGURE 5-1. Bodily changes in pregnancy: (*a*) nonpregnant; (*b*) one month; (*c*) six months; (*d*) nine months.

Now the well-developed muscles of the uterus begin to contract rhythmically, pushing the baby's head gently against the cervix. This is called "labor." The contractions are repeated several times an hour at first, and then more frequently. The pressure gradually opens the cervix. Now the mother can help, for she can consciously exert extra pressure with the muscles of her diaphragm and abdominal wall. Soon she has pushed the head out, and the rest of the body follows easily. After the umbilical cord is cut, the baby takes his first breath, announcing to the world that from now on he will do his own breathing. A few more contractions expel the placenta, and the mother's body begins to revert to its nonpregnant condition.

There is much variation in length of labor, bodily changes, position of the baby, and every other part of the process. Some imperil the life of the mother. The fact that nearly all pregnancies (aside from the considerable number that miscarry in the first few months) now end happily is a tribute to the medical profession. Today most women in American cities realize the importance of seeing the doctor early and regularly during pregnancy so that incipient trouble can be recognized and of going to a hospital to have their babies. In a hospital, equipment and skill are available in case of trouble, and the baby can be removed through an incision in the abdomen (Cesarean section) if necessary.

The human baby is carried internally longer—in comparison with its size—than practically any other mammal. Strangely enough, it is also true that a newborn human baby is at an earlier stage of its development than any other placental mammal. The reason for this is the great overdevelopment of one of our organs—the brain. Nine months of pregnancy are insufficient for the full maturing of this most human of human organs, for it is not only large but extremely complex. When a baby is born, its head is greatly out of proportion to the rest of its body, but even so it is underdeveloped—by human standards. If the baby were carried until its body was at a stage of development comparable with other mammals, the head would be too large to pass out of the vagina. For a year after the baby is born, the seams of its skull remain soft to allow for further growth. Most newborn mammals stand after a few hours and run after a few days, but in a human baby muscular development must wait until the crucial job of forming a human brain is completed.

It has often been asked why civilized women need a doctor's care all through pregnancy and concentrated attention during delivery, while primitive women get along without it. Actually this inferiority is only an illusion. Before it was usual for a woman to have prenatal care, and to this day in primitive communities, many women became sick and even died as a result of pregnancies. They developed toxemias, chemical poisonings of the blood due to metabolic changes during pregnancy; today doctors discover these conditions early by tests of urine and take steps to avoid trouble. Women never knew until they were actually in labor whether their anatomy would permit them to pass the child normally; today the doctor knows in advance and will perform a Cesarean section if necessary.

In the past, women sometimes bled to death if delivery was unusually difficult; today, blood transfusions replace the lost blood, while sutures and special drugs help to control the bleeding. Where once infections occurred during delivery, today antiseptic techniques make this rare, and antibiotics control infection if it does occur. Modern techniques have corrected deficiencies that have probably existed since man appeared on earth, a creature with a head so large that it could not be expelled easily through a normal vagina.

In one respect, however, modern woman does seem to be inferior to her primitive counterparts. She *expects* childbirth to be painful and difficult, for she has had no experience with the process, while primitive women see birth taking place frequently and are unafraid. The fear alone creates pain and difficulty. Have you ever been worried or frightened so much that the muscles of your stomach tightened until you experienced a violent cramp? Can you imagine how much worse this might be if a large object in your stomach prevented the contraction of these muscles? The uterus may react in the same way.

Modern medical practice refuses to concede the need for pain in childbirth, and severe pain can be eased in modern hospitals. Mild anesthetics and tranquilizers are always on hand. Hypnotism in the hands of a competent doctor, applied to a susceptible subject, can make even drugs unnecessary.

In the past few years, efforts have been made to remove the cause of pain. In this country, the practice is called "natural childbirth," although "educated childbirth" would be a better name. The pregnant woman studies both her pregnancy and the delivery that must follow. She takes exercises to strengthen muscles she will have to use when the day comes. Like a good actor, she has studied her part and knows what to do when the curtain goes up. She will relax between contractions, so that her muscles will not become tense. During the second part of labor, she will actively help by bringing her abdominal muscles into play. Since she knows what to expect, she does not feel the muscle-tightening anxiety that produces so much of the pain. Her husband may be allowed to stay with her to lend moral support and a loving hand to hold. And she also obtains comfort from the knowledge that anesthetics are available if she feels that she needs them.

Today, an understanding and intelligent woman can make her childbearing nearly as simple as a cow or dog, whose babies do not have big heads. Women who have delivered babies while fully conscious invariably consider this to be one of the greatest experiences of their lives. The boundless joy of creativity can be felt by many people in many areas of work, but the ultimate thrill of creating a human life is something no man can ever experience.

CHILDREN BY CHOICE

It is nearly unheard of for a woman to feel no emotion on discovering that she is pregnant. She may feel a boundless joy or a bottomless desperation, depending on whether she is a happily married woman with strong maternal feelings or an unmarried girl who went just a little too far. A woman may go through a long series of treatments to enable her to become pregnant; at some other stage of her life she may take measures to avoid pregnancy, or even to end an existing pregnancy. Whatever else it may be, the coming of a baby is never a neutral event. Most people, when they marry, anticipate joy in raising a family, but they want children at an appropriate time and in some limited number. Whatever decisions they make, medical science can help. If fertility is low, treatment is available. And the majority of married couples in the United States today take some steps to avoid pregnancy when it is not desired. Steps taken to prevent pregnancy are known as *contraception.*

Methods of contraception fall into three broad categories. The most obvious is abstention from sexual intercourse. This is highly recommended for unmarried people, but it will never be popular with the married ones. In the *rhythm method,* couples abstain during the wife's fertile days each month. The trouble with this method, which is the only one approved by the Catholic church, is the difficulty of knowing when these days occur.

A second method, most widely used today, is to prevent the sperms from reaching the egg. This can be accomplished by a mechanical device worn either by the man or woman during intercourse. Doctors and birth control clinics will help people who wish to use this method, but the sale of mechanical contraceptives is illegal in two of our states, Connecticut and Massachusetts. Other states may put legal barriers in the way of distributing these devices, but not so completely. Like many laws on our books, these are not enforced, and contraceptive devices are in use all over the country. The laws are now being challenged in the courts, and may have been found unconstitutional or repealed by the time you read this.

There has been a recent revival of interest in devices that are inserted into the uterus and left there more-or-less permanently. Little silver buttons were used in this way, but have been abandoned because they produce irritation and bleeding. Recent tests of plastic devices that were inserted by doctors in 19,000 Japanese women and left there for many years have been highly encouraging. They are safe and nonirritating, highly effective, and do not interfere with normal pregnancy if removed.

More drastic interference with the passage of sperms is accomplished by surgically closing the fallopian tubes of a woman or the sperm ducts of a man, an operation called "sterilization." This works well, but it has a major disadvantage: it is usually irreversible. Anyone who might some day want another child should not be sterilized. The operation is illegal in several states and violates religious principles in some groups. Furthermore, many hospitals will not allow it to be performed except for sound medical reasons.

A fourth method of contraception is medical treatment to prevent eggs or sperms from forming. A progesterone-like tablet for this purpose is now widely used, but it has certain drawbacks. It is expensive, for the tablets must be taken twenty-four days out of every month, and even then it is not one hundred per cent effective. It seems to be harmless, but the United States Pure Food and Drug Administration is not sure and has approved its use for two years only. Also, it has unfavorable side effects in many women. Attempts to develop treatment of this sort for men have been only partly successful. These treatments seem always to allow a full return to fertility when they are discontinued.

No method of contraception is foolproof, especially if not carefully used. The desire to avoid having a child is often so strong that a pregnant woman will go to almost any lengths to destroy the embryo she is carrying, a procedure known as *artificial abortion*. Every nation has its traditional methods of producing abortion, using various drugs or mechanical stimulation. Those that are effective are highly dangerous; those that are safe usually do not work. The only safe and effective method of producing an artificial abortion is by surgically scraping the uterus, a process that can be carried out only by a doctor in a hospital, and then only if the pregnancy is no more than a few weeks old.

In the United States, every state considers it a major crime to perform an abortion unless several doctors will certify that it is necessary to save the life or health of the mother. Many countries do not restrict abortions, and in Japan, for example, it is done in government clinics at the request of the woman. There are over a million illegal abortions in the United States every year, most of them performed by incompetent people under unsanitary conditions. As a result, many women die every year of the same three causes that used to kill women in childbirth: hemorrhage, shock, and infection. Unless Americans decide to accept artificial abortion publicly and make it legal, it is not to be considered as a method of birth control.

SEX IN HUMAN LIFE

Given the bodies of a representative selection of animals to dissect, our Martian friend would probably decide that man is an animal, different only in unessential details from other animals. But if he were to study its behavior instead of its anatomy, he would conclude that the human species is unique. Its most unusual anatomical feature—the greatly outsize brain—endows the species with patterns of behavior that are impossible for any other animal. We found in Chapter 2 that some animals can adapt to a wider range of environmental conditions than others, but in this regard, as in so many others, man is unique. People make their homes in temperate climates and tropical islands, in the deserts of Africa and frozen tundras of the arctic. Each population adopts a way of life suited to its environment. Our brains are our key to survival, for we can improvise our food and shelter, our clothing and protection from materials at hand. The brain controlling the hand that makes and uses tools creatively is the combination that gives man his supremacy in the world.

Every animal population must cope with its environment in order to survive. Food must be obtained, enemies avoided, protection and shelter found, and new generations raised. The means to do these things, in animals, are part of the biological endowment. The lion uses his teeth, claws, and muscles to get his dinner. He can do this in only one way, because he is built for a particular life. But man can make the tools to enable him to live in many ways. A child growing up learns to use the tools of his society. An Eskimo boy learns to hunt walruses with a harpoon and to make a kayak and an igloo. Every society teaches its children how to work, how to think and feel, how to relate to parents, brothers, friends, and spouses. To study any aspect of human life, it is important to investigate the process by which the group trains the minds and hands of its members.

The versatility of the brain-hand-tools combination is seen in human reproduction, as well as all other human behavior. A primitive woman may have her baby on the floor of a hut, but there will always be other women helping her. We may deplore the obstetric techniques used, but the basic human phenomena are there: each society has its own techniques which are handed down from generation to generation. And the techniques are social ones, for no woman must have her baby alone. Over the centuries, the methods have improved. Each generation has made changes in methods of helping women deliver and has communicated these changes to the next. This has culminated in the highly educated brain-hand-tools of a doctor in a modern hospital. In this aspect of human behavior, as in all others, what people think and do is controlled more by their society than by their biology. Social control comes with social responsibility, and each generation learns the methods and ideas of its parents and improves on them.

Social responsibility for reproduction is not limited to obstetric help. Illegitimate children, offspring of broken homes, maltreated, neglected, deserted, and orphaned children are not left to make their own way, but are cared for. In our culture these children are the concern of social agencies, supported by tax money and voluntary contributions. A hundred years ago, half the children born in the world died before reaching the age of ten, mainly in the first year. Medical care has drastically changed this picture in the civilized world and is now changing it in the rest of the world as well.

As human history is made, social responsibility spreads to encompass more people. The health of the people of the world is the domain of the World Health Organization. This has created a new problem, one which has never existed for any species. It is called the "population explosion."

Think about your own neighborhood. How many fields and forests have given way to houses in the past ten years? The population of the world doubled between 1840 and 1920 and is expected to double again by 1980. The excess of births over deaths now amounts to about fifty million a year, and the rate of population increase is itself increasing. The world was shocked when a single atom bomb snuffed out one hundred thousand lives in Hiroshima in 1945; this loss of population is made up in a single day's excess births. One mathematician has calculated that the world will come to an end on the thirteenth day of November, 2026. He reached this astonishing conclusion by plotting a graph of the world's population and extending into the future. On that day, according to him, the population of the world will become infinite!

No animal species could face such a problem. As the

population of any animal species increases, the numbers of individuals are kept down by spread of disease due to increased crowding, by a shortage of food, or by an increase in predators that use the animal for food. The coming of civilization has drastically reduced the effectiveness of such controls on human population. When our ancestors ten thousand years ago invented agriculture, they found a reliable source of food that could support a great increase in population. In spite of frequent famines and chronic undernourishment of most people of the world, shortage of food has never been a decisive factor in the control of human population. The effective control has been disease, but medical science has now eliminated this control as well.

In a sense, human nature made the population explosion inevitable. It is in the nature of man to co-operate on an ever-wider scale to produce continuous improvement in the use of his brain-hand-tools to control his environment. Science has taught us to raise food in the desert, to produce clothing and houses suitable to all climates, to escape the destructive effects of disease. Today, there are more and more people coming to believe that science must be put to work on a world-wide basis to control the human population. Nuclear warfare is the only other visible alternative to breeding ourselves off the face of the earth.

The idea of population control is not new. Most primitive peoples practice some form of control, especially in time of famine. Their efforts fall into three general categories: contraception, abortion, and infanticide. No civilized people has ever accepted infanticide, but both contraception and abortion are widely practiced in the civilized world. The population explosion has made this a problem to be solved socially, rather than on an individual basis as heretofore. Some countries, especially in the Far East, have made a start. Japan has set up a group of clinics where legalized abortions and voluntary sterilizations are performed and birth control information is disseminated. This all-out attack on the problem has made Japan the only country in the Orient whose population growth in the fifties was less than twenty per cent. India is starting on a program of sterilization and birth control. Even predominantly Catholic Poland has a birth control program that has met with considerable success.

SEX AND CULTURE

The science of agriculture and the art of cooking have elevated eating from a biological necessity to a source of esthetic satisfaction. A meal is more than a means of filling an empty belly; it gives pleasure to our noses, eyes, and mouths and a quiet, congenial occasion to communicate with our families and friends. A home is not merely a form of protection from the elements; it is a comfortable place to live in, an island of security in an unstable world, a place for good books and warm social relations.

As soon as esthetics enters the picture, so does individual variation. All men may agree on what is nourishing, but they will not agree on what is tasty. Taste is a highly individual matter, for which, we are told, there is no accounting, but this is not entirely true. Your tastes are formed by your experiences in society. You and I might disagree as to whether a pizza pie and a milk shake constitute a satisfactory lunch, but neither of us will go for a smoked rat or a mess of grilled locusts; yet both of these foods are delicacies in other societies.

Courtship and mating have also been humanized. One result has been an increase in the importance of sex in our lives, compared with animals. Most animals are sexually active only during a short breeding season, but people have no season. To a male dog, a bitch is just another dog unless she is in heat; to a man, a woman is always a woman. Can you think of any occasion on which you have not been acutely conscious of the sex of your companion? For animals, sex is just one part of the reproductive process; for people it is a source of satisfactions that are fundamentally human. We enjoy the sexual content of our literature and the beauties of the human form in pictures, all the way from the old masters to the advertisements in yesterday's magazines. Our sex lives have become intertwined with the most delightful feelings of love for boy or girl friend, husband or wife, and, eventually, children.

Since we are dealing with a human process, we should expect it to vary greatly in various cultures, and we will certainly find this to be true. An Arab with four wives may be highly respected; an American with a mere two is put in jail. In many cultures, girls (and, much more rarely, boys) are expected to be virgins when they marry; a Polynesian girl is not considered a good "catch" until she has proven her fertility by having a baby. Homosexuality is a crime and a disgrace in America, but in other cultures it may be almost universally practiced, nearly completely unknown, the most exalted form of sexual activity (as in ancient Greece), or a sign of a special mystical gift. In some societies, masturbation is considered normal; in others, it is cause for ridicule or punishment.

With all this variation in sexual customs, there are certain features that are nearly universal. One of these is the family. A Polynesian youth is completely promiscuous, but, when he grows older, he settles down to a more-or-less monogamous life and raises a family. Polygamy, where it exists, is a privilege of the upper classes, not the way of life of the large mass of people. People in all societies seem to find that single marriage—a more-or-less permanent union involving financial arrangements, sex, reproduction, and the raising of children in co-operation with one other person—provides the greatest satisfaction of all the possible alternative ways of life. From what we know of how sexuality develops, this is probably because children raised in the intimacy of a good family, in an atmosphere of love, grow up into adults capable of emotions that make enduring sexual love possible. The monogamous family is a self-perpetuating institution.

SEXUAL DEVELOPMENT IN OUR SOCIETY

Our society, like all others, has developed a set of standards of sex behavior and a social context that produces a particular kind of sex life. Sex training starts early, for most children learn very young that there is a special, pleasant feeling derived from stimulation of their sex organs. This self-stimulation may continue throughout childhood and may lead children to explore each other's genitals as well. Similar behavior is found in animals, but the emotional part of sex life also starts in infancy. The warm, intimate feelings that a parent experiences in holding a child are felt by the child as well. This is not usually thought of as a sexual feeling, but it is akin to the sexual feeling between man and wife. To a man, the love of his child may be a kind of extension of his love for his wife, for the child is their child.

This physical contact is vitally important to the well-being of the child, and children deprived of it in institutions have been known to waste away and even die of the deprivation. It has another importance, for it is a form of sexual training. The child is learning to feel the love and security of warm physical contact. Psychologists have found that a child's early relationships with his parents have a crucial effect on later attitudes toward everybody, and most especially on sexual adjustment.

In the infant, love expressed in physical contact and

genital stimulation are sharply separated from each other, and the genital feelings come from himself, not from those he loves. As he grows, his emotional world widens and he will express his love feelings toward others. When a group of girls walk down the street with their arms around each other, they are helping their friendship along by adding physical contact to the other factors that bind them together. At different ages, children relate in different ways to those of the same sex and those of the opposite sex. Boys and girls who play indiscriminately together at the age of six separate into two groups by the time they are nine. The boys tease the girls and the girls pretend to ignore the boys. These children, moving implacably toward their adolescence, are passing through a period of homosexual friendships, usually with little or no sex activity. This "latent" period has long been a part of normal emotional growth, and many psychologists are alarmed by the tendency they see today to eliminate it by starting mixed parties and dating at ever-earlier ages.

Adolescence is a crisis, a time of rapid change. At the age of twelve or thirteen, a boy's sex hormones start to flow and the external genitals soon triple in size. Semen begins to flow from the seminal vesicles and the prostate gland, and the boy begins to feel urgent sexual desires. Quite often, these desires will dominate a boy's thoughts whenever he is not actively involved in something else. There is a severe disharmony between our culture and our biology at this time, for our society makes no allowance for sexual activity at this age, in spite of the fact that it is biologically inevitable if a boy is normal. Nearly all boys masturbate during their adolescence, and most of them also experience emissions of semen at night during erotic dreams.

Girls also develop sexual potency at about this time, but they do not usually experience the same kind of urgency.

A majority of girls masturbate, but they are more likely to think of boys in terms of love, tenderness, home and family than simply as sex partners.

This is not to say that all adolescent boys or girls are alike, or that they should be. While one boy treats every girl as though he needed only the seduction merit badge to make Eagle Scout, his friend down the block is busy with the basketball team. And one girl may be worried only about what might happen to her party dress in the car after the dance, while her friend couldn't care less. Adolescents are traditionally unpredictable, mainly because at this age people are experimenting, trying to find themselves, adopting one personality one day and another the next to see which fits best. A fairly large number of people experiment with homosexuality in adolescence, and perhaps most of them think about it, wondering about themselves and their friends. They do not discuss their sex problems, for they often mistrust their elders, and they often feel completely alone and different.

Sexual maturity is reached several years before marriage is possible, and in our culture marriage is the only socially acceptable outlet for the sex drives. The problem is not only financial, for marriage requires an emotional maturity and responsibility that is rare in adolescents. This places a severe burden on young people. For the first time, they realize that they are growing up, that they must plan a career and a life. And those exciting, delightful, and annoying biological urges keep getting in the way.

Through experimentation, people can win their way through to maturity. As relationships with the opposite sex become easier, homosexual impulses fade into the background, although they do not usually disappear. Every man sometimes prefers the company of men; every woman feels a closeness and sympathy with women that a man cannot hope to share. The adolescent carries his preadolescent friendships with him and will never lose them altogether. A normal adult directs the specifically sexual content of friendship to the opposite sex, but he can accept occasional homosexual urges without acting on them or worrying about them.

The experimentation and confusion of adolescence lead to a more stable adulthood in which plans and goals are harmonized. Part of this maturity is the coming of sexual love. The sexual attraction, at first quite general, becomes fused with the need for closeness, for a personal intimacy to be shared by one other person. As a young man or woman matures, the need for love and the need for sex unite to become a desire for that most intimate of all kinds of contact, sexual intercourse in the context of a continuing love-relationship. In due time, two people find that they meet each other's needs and join together for their mutual benefit. Each becomes for the other a refuge from an uncertain world, a partner in the difficult task of building an independent life. Their love and need for each other are repeatedly reinforced by physical closeness and by the increasing pleasure each derives from the other in their sex relations. Sexual love in marriage is the uniquely human development of the sexual process.

Unfortunately, not everyone grows up emotionally. The pattern of development outlined above can be drastically upset by early experiences. A boy with an inadequate father may never learn how to be a man and may become homosexual. Or he may learn from a brutal and punitive mother to hate women, with the same result. Children lacking in love in their homes may never learn what love means and may grow up to be promiscuous adults. Children threatened with dire consequences from masturbation or other sexual activity may become so anxious about their sex lives that they are unable to form a real sex-love relationship. But those who can form a marriage based on mutual need and mutual help can find the ultimate joys of sex in a rich and satisfying monogamous sexual love.

6

Egg and Sperm

We have taken a long and careful look at the processes by which new generations of life arise. Now it is time to put these processes under a microscope, to investigate in detail the cellular, subcellular, and eventually the chemical processes that form the foundation of the reproduction of organisms.

The concept of fertilization as a union of a single egg and a single sperm is so much a part of common knowledge today that it is hard to believe that this knowledge is less than a hundred years old. But since a human sperm, including its long, slender tail, is no more than a twentieth the size of this comma, and a human egg is considerably smaller than a period, neither sperms nor eggs could have been known until the microscope was perfected and widely used. And even after these cells were discovered, it took many years to determine the part that each one plays.

Eggs have always been known. Aristotle studied the

reproductive processes of many animals and was familiar with the eggs of birds, amphibians, and insects, among others. But he singled out a separate category, a group which he called "internally viviparous" animals, distinguished by the fact that they bore young without producing eggs. This group, which included man, corresponds to what we today call mammals. Aristotle also wrote extensively about human reproduction. He knew, of course, that the embryo is carried in its mother's womb and is born through the vagina. He also knew that it is nourished by blood passed to it through the umbilical cord, although he thought that the blood belonged to the mother. The idea that the developing embryo forms its own blood was still two thousand years away.

In Aristotle's time, there were two conflicting theories of the origin of the embryo of human beings and other mammals, and both theories had adherents through the Middle Ages. The first great physician, Hippocrates, developed the *two-seed theory*. This was based on the observation that both man and woman produce secretions during sexual intercourse, the semen of the man and the vaginal secretions of the woman. Hippocrates surmised that these two fluids unite and coagulate into a solid mass of material. This coagulum, nourished by the mother's blood, was supposed to gradually develop structure, changing from a formless, cheesy mass into a baby. To the present day, primitive peoples and even ignorant people in highly developed societies commonly believe in a theory of this sort. They do not realize that the vaginal secretions play no part at all in the growth of the embryo, that pregnancy and birth can be completely normal even if these secretions are lacking.

Aristotle advanced a different idea, the *one-seed theory*. In this theory, the vaginal secretions play no part, and the role of the mother in the reproductive process is greater than that of the father. Aristotle noted that the flow of menstrual blood stops during pregnancy and that blood flows through the umbilical cord into the embryo. He surmised that the embryo forms out of the mother's blood, which would pass out of the body at the time of menstruation if the woman were not pregnant. The semen organizes and forms the mother's undischarged menstrual blood, giving it the properties of a living being that eventually grows into a baby. This theory sounds naïve to us today, but there are rather remarkable elements of truth in it. It is true that the vaginal fluid has nothing to do with the embryo. In a sense it is true that the embryo forms from the mother's blood, for the growing embryo assimilates the food materials that are carried to it in the blood. And it is unquestionably true that the male parent contributes an organizing element, although we now realize that this is not all the semen, but only a single sperm.

As was typical of the scholarship of the Middle Ages, these theories were the subject of endless and sterile argument. No decision between them could be reached until the problem attracted the attention of a great experimental biologist.

THE DISCOVERY OF FERTILIZATION

William Harvey, royal physician to King James I of England and later to his successor, Charles I, was a well-known and highly respected biologist in his own day. He is best remembered for his discovery that blood circulates through the body, flowing out of the heart through arteries and back to the heart through veins. He surmised the existence, later shown microscopically, of capillaries, miniscule vessels that carry the blood from the tiniest end branches of the arteries into the smallest veins. Harvey interested himself in many other biological problems as well, including reproduction. In 1651 he published his last great work, a book called *De*

Generatione Animalium. The frontispiece of this book was a picture of Zeus holding an egg-shaped container from which various animals were emerging. The container bore the inscription *Ex ovo omnia* — "everything from the egg" —which epitomized the conclusions about reproduction which he arrived at after many years of experimentation.

Twenty years before Redi bred his maggots in rotten meat, Harvey was denying the possibility of spontaneous generation and simultaneously rejecting both the two-seed and one-seed theories by stating that all creatures originate in eggs. As we shall see, this dictum goes too far, as new ideas often do, but it was a great advance for his day.

It was an old experiment with hen's eggs that prepared Harvey's mind for the conclusions he reached about mammalian reproduction. He obtained a group of fertilized hen's eggs and opened one each day in order to study the stages in the development of the egg up to the eventual hatching. He was by no means the first to do this; in fact it was done by a student of Hippocrates in ancient Greece and had been repeated several times since. (There is a story that Cleopatra did a similar experiment on humans, using slave girls as subjects, but it may not be true.) Previous workers had reported that the entire mass of the egg gradually takes on the form of a chick, and this was used as evidence for the ancient theories of mammalian reproduction, the coagulum of male and female fluids taking the place of the egg contents. But Harvey observed without preconceived ideas and was aided by a hand lens. He discovered that the embryo of the chick is at first extremely tiny and grows by using the white and yolk of the egg as food. He thought of the egg proper as being a tiny speck of living matter, invisible at first, then growing at the expense of stored food that fills the eggshell.

In later years, Harvey performed a similar experiment

on mammals, using the deer in the king's shooting preserve as experimental subjects. He simply killed and dissected does shortly after they mated in the spring. According to either of the old theories, he should have found a mass of coagulated semen and blood or of semen and vaginal secretions, filling the uterus and beginning to convert itself into a fawn. He found nothing at all!

Game wardens protested that the does were not pregnant, that the weather had been unusual and had prevented nature from taking its usual course. Harvey then used a technique that was still in its infancy: the controlled experiment. He mated a large number of does and divided them into two groups. The control group was isolated and allowed to live normally; when they brought forth their young at the usual time, it was clear that the matings had been successful. But once again, there was no visible embryo in does dissected soon after mating. Clearly these deer must have been just as pregnant as the others, and it became obvious that the embryo at that stage was simply too small to be found. Harvey postulated that the embryo formed from a tiny egg, just as the chick embryo formed from an extremely small bit of living substance that makes up the vital part of a hen's egg. His experiments were so clearly done and so well presented that both the two-seed and the one-seed theories soon became historical curiosities.

The microscope was coming into general use about that time, and before long, tiny capsules were found in the ovaries of mammals. These *Graafian follicles* were then thought to be the eggs that Harvey reasoned must be present. We now realize that they are not the eggs themselves, but that each capsule produces a single egg. The principle, however, was soon accepted, and in spite of the error in detail, Aristotle's concept of mammals as eggless creatures was laid to rest within a few years. It was not until the nineteenth century that the very early embryos of a dog were found and successive stages in their history were traced from the ovary through the fallopian tube and into the uterus.

Thus was half of the problem of sexual reproduction solved. But what of the other half? By what mysterious influence does the semen of a male animal activate the egg and start it on its development into an embryo? Some sixteen years after the publication of Harvey's great work on reproduction, the greatest microscopist of his day, Anton van Leeuwenhoek, reported on his studies of animal semen, including man's. He found in the male sexual fluid enormous numbers of "animalcules," tiny cells swimming freely by means of long tails. It took a long time to establish the nature of these animalcules, for similar creatures could be found in scrapings from teeth, or in stagnant water for that matter!

It was eventually shown that only one kind of "animal" appeared in the semen of a given species, whereas other sources yielded a wide variety of protozoa and bacteria. The nature of these sperms was proven when it was shown that semen is not capable of rendering a female animal pregnant if these "animalcules" are filtered out.

In the ensuing years, eggs and sperms were found in many creatures: roundworms, flowering plants, insects, ferns, a limitless variety of creatures using the same mechanism to initiate their new generations. But for over two hundred years, the exact nature of the fertilization process remained a mystery. It was not until 1875 that the German anatomist Oscar Hertwig succeeded finally in observing fertilization. He was studying the reproduction of the sea urchin (Figure 6-1), a spiny-skinned relative of the starfish, found in the Mediterranean. This creature produces eggs small enough to be studied conveniently under the microscope. The eggs, furthermore, are fertilized in the open water, so that Hertwig could put eggs and sperms on the stage of his microscope and watch what happened. It was this study that established for the first time what is now known to be universally true: many sperms approach the egg, but fertilization is accomplished by a single sperm which penetrates into and unites with the egg.

FIGURE 6-1. Sea urchin.

HOW AN EGG IS FERTILIZED

Following Hertwig's original description of fertilization, many research workers investigated the fertilization process. It has turned out to be far more complex than anyone in Hertwig's day could have imagined. Much of the work has been done on the same animal that Hertwig used, the sea urchin, and the related starfishes have also proved useful. Certain marine worms have also been studied thoroughly and work is now being done on mammalian fertilization. Large eggs like those of birds and reptiles, and even the eighth-inch-long eggs of frogs and many fish are too big to be studied in detail under a microscope, and there are no details known of how they are fertilized.

Several mammal eggs, including that of man, have been successfully fertilized *in vitro,* that is, in a test tube. Human eggs were obtained from women who had to undergo surgical removal of the ovaries and fallopian tubes, which carry the mammalian eggs from the ovary to the uterus. Eggs were obtained by doing the operation shortly after the eggs left the ovaries. It is at this time that the eggs are normally fertilized, and the eggs were fertilized *in vitro* by putting sperms on them. Both the fertilization of the egg and its earliest stages of development have been directly observed under the microscope. The zygotes have been kept alive for several days in a medium made from human body fluids. One human embryo was raised *in vitro* for twenty-nine days and was destroyed then only because it began to show abnormalities of structure.

It is unfortunate that it has been necessary to confine studies of fertilization to a small number of animal species. It would be a blunder to generalize conclusions reached from these studies. Life is full of surprises, and the biologist who studies life never knows what he will find when he extends his studies to a different species.

The sperms of plants vary widely. Sperms of algae are often propelled by two or more flagella, and those of ferns and cycads are covered with a great many. The red algae produce sperms with no method of propulsion, relying on water currents to carry them to the egg. In both the fungi and the pollen tube of the seed plants, the sperm does not swim, but consists simply of a nucleus that is delivered to the egg by the growth of a filament.

Animal sperms also vary, but most seem to consist of the same parts. With the exception of the ameboid sperms of roundworms, all animal sperms are propelled by a single flagellum. The human sperm shown in Figure 6-2 is typical of animal sperms. It consists of a small, dense head which is mainly nucleus, a short mid-section, and a long, thin tail. The front part of the nucleus is covered by a cap, the *acrosome,* which has important functions in getting the sperm into the egg. The mid-section contains the *mitochondria,* the special structures that produce the energy of every cell. The tail consists of a capsule containing several axial threads which extend a little distance beyond the end of the capsule. The only function of the tail seems to be the propulsion of the sperm. Tail and all, a man's entire biological contribution to the next generation is only a couple of thousandths of an inch long.

FIGURE 6-2. Human sperm magnified 2,000 times.

The human egg (Figure 6-3) is like that of other animals and not much different from that of a sea urchin. It is a slightly elongated spheroid about a hundredth of an inch long, containing a large nucleus a little distance from its center. A large part of the cytoplasm is filled with granules of yolk, a fatty material that comprises the food of the embryo for its first few days. The egg is surrounded by a thin, clear, gelatinous layer, which in turn is covered by

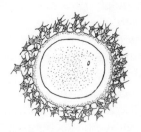

FIGURE 6-3. Human egg surrounded by follicle cells. Magnified 100 times.

several layers of cells derived from the follicle in which the egg was formed in the ovary.

Sea urchin eggs are similar but are surrounded only by a jelly-like material rather than the two layers that cover a mammalian egg. The egg of a bird, on the other hand, is different. The chief difference is in the amount of food stored. A young bird must find food for itself within a few days after it hatches, and must, therefore, be large and well developed when it emerges from the shell. It needs an enormous amount of food during its development, food which it cannot obtain from its mother as a mammalian embryo does. The egg cell proper is what is called the "yolk" of the egg, for the egg emerges from the ovary with a great deal of this rich and nourishing material. As it passes down the oviduct, additional food in the form of albumen ("egg white") is deposited around the egg cell.

FUNCTIONS OF THE SPERM

The tiny sperms bear a big responsibility in the continuity of life. They must perform at least five distinct functions, all of them now subjects of intensive investigation. The sperm must (1) swim to the egg; (2) penetrate the membranes that surround the egg; (3) attach itself to the egg surface; (4) *activate* the egg (that is, cause the egg to start its development); and (5) provide a nucleus that combines with the egg nucleus to help control the development of the embryo.

First, how does the sperm swim to the egg? The motive power is supplied by the axial filaments of the tail, which act like the flagella of bacteria or protozoa. These filaments are protein fibers that are able to contract, something like the fibers within muscle cells that produce the motion of animals. But how does the sperm manage to point its head toward the egg?

The stimulus that directs the sperms of ferns, mosses, and certain algae has been found. The egg of the common brake fern secretes a simple organic chemical, malic acid, which diffuses through the water on the lower surface of the sexual plant. Since the substance is produced in the egg, the concentration of malic acid is greatest near the egg and decreases with distance from the egg. The sperms have some mechanism (completely unknown) that causes them to turn in such a way as to present their head ends toward the greatest concentration of malic acid. These sperms will swim just as eagerly toward a drop of malic acid placed in the water as toward an egg. Different plants use various chemicals for this purpose; mosses use sucrose, the same kind of sugar that you keep in a bowl on your dinner table.

No such mechanism has been found in any animal. An extract of ground sea urchin eggs placed in water with millions of sperms leaves the sperms completely uninterested. It has been shown, in fact, that the movement of these sperms is completely at random, that the sperm touches the egg surface only by accident! The eggs are fertilized successfully only because of the great numbers involved; with hundreds of eggs and hundreds of millions of sperms near each other in the water, few eggs escape.

It might seem foolhardy to assert that the eggs exert *no* attraction for the sperms, but mathematical analysis makes the conclusion inescapable. If a known number of sperms are placed in a known volume of water with a known number of eggs, and the average speed of the sperms is measured, it is possible to calculate how many eggs will be struck in one minute, how many in two minutes, and so on. The mathematics is identical to the method that a physicist would use to determine how many molecules of a gas would strike a given surface area in a given time. The experimental check is made by counting the number of eggs fertilized in the first minute, the first two minutes, etc. The measured fertilizations agree with the assumption that the sperms move at random, but not with the assumption that their motion is directed. This is only one of many areas in which probability theory has invaded biology.

The same mathematical theory tells us that random motion will *not* account for the fertilization of mammalian eggs. A male rat produces hundreds of millions of sperms at a mating, just as a sea urchin does, but only about one hundred of them succeed in penetrating from the vagina through the uterus into the fallopian tubes. Nevertheless, each of the half-dozen or so eggs in the fallopian tube usually gets fertilized. So far, there is no evidence pointing to any mechanism that directs the sperms of a rat to the eggs.

The second function of the sperm is the penetration of the various jellies and membranes that invest the egg. This process is well known and seems to be uniform in a variety of creatures. The acrosome of the sperm of a sea urchin produces an enzyme that digests the jelly surrounding the egg. Mammal sperms digest the cementing material that holds cells together in tissues, so they can penetrate the layers of cells surrounding the egg. Even in flowering plants this mechanism is used, for the pollen tube grows through the tissues of the pistil by digesting a path for itself.

Third, the sperm must fasten itself to the surface of the egg. As the sperm approaches the egg, a tiny thread, which can be seen in Figure 6-4, is extruded from the acrosome. This *sperm filament* was first seen under a microscope many years ago, but later investigators were unable to find it and preferred to believe that the original describer had an overactive imagination. The electron microscope has settled the question decisively: the sperm filament exists and has been extensively studied. It becomes fastened to the surface of

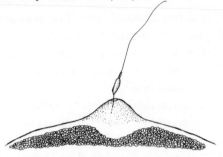

FIGURE 6-4. Sperm entering egg.

the egg, and the motion of the sperm then stops.

Fourth, the egg must be activated. The sperm does not have to enter the egg to activate it. If the sperm is removed just after it has become attached to the surface of the egg, the egg will undergo its typical post-fertilization changes. The difficulty of discovering just what the sperm does to the surface of the egg is complicated by the fact that the egg can also be activated by a jab with a needle, by high temperature, by low temperature, by too much or too little salt in the water, or by any of a long list of chemicals! These eggs may then develop by parthenogenesis. The artificially activated eggs of sea urchins or frogs usually die long before they grow to maturity—but not always! Many ways have been found to activate eggs in the laboratory, but it has so far proven impossible to find out how the sperms themselves go about it.

Fifth, the sperm must contribute its nucleus to the zygote. Shortly after the sperm nucleus enters the egg, it disappears. It soon appears again, much enlarged, so that it looks more like the egg nucleus. The sperm nucleus then becomes surrounded by an *aster,* a mass of fibers formed in the egg cytoplasm, radiating outward, with the sperm nucleus at its center. As the aster grows, the increase in length of the rays pushes the sperm nucleus to the center of the egg, where it meets and unites with the egg nucleus. Only then is the fertilization process complete.

Activation of the egg and union of nuclei are two distinct and separable processes. For development to start, it is sufficient that the sperm touches the outer surface of the egg. But the course of development of any organism is controlled by the nuclei of the cells of the body. This is what we mean when we say that the hereditary characteristics are carried in the nucleus. This nucleus contains only half—exactly half—of the hereditary material needed for normal development, so the embryo usually dies unless the other half is supplied by the sperm. Egg and sperm have entirely different functions in the fertilization process, but their nuclei are completely equivalent in control of subsequent development.

FUNCTIONS OF THE EGG

The egg, like the sperm, has many roles to play in the drama of fertilization. It must (1) store food for the developing embryo; (2) receive a sperm; (3) become activated; (4) reject all other sperms; (5) provide half a nucleus; and (6) develop into an embryo.

First, food storage. All eggs store some food, and some eggs store a great deal. In the tiny sea urchin or mammalian egg, yolk granules are uniformly distributed throughout the cytoplasm, while in the larger egg of a frog, the food is mainly confined to the lower half. In the large eggs of birds, yolk occupies all the egg cell (as distinct from the "egg" that includes shell, membranes, and albumen) except for the microscopic bit of cytoplasm enclosing a nucleus that forms a spot on one side.

Second, the egg must receive the sperm. It was at first believed that the sperm swims in some directed way to the egg and then actively bores through the egg surface. This idea may have been encouraged by the active swimming movements of the sperm before it touches the egg and by the apparent passivity of the egg. Perhaps it was supported by the well-known sexual aggressiveness of males, both human and animal, and the passiveness of the females. We now know that the egg is by no means inactive in the fertilization process. But the analogy is still good, for the sexual passivity of female animals—and humans—is also superficial, concealing a very real interest. Among gametes, as among animals and people, he chases her until she catches him.

Many plants, as we have seen, produce eggs that secrete chemicals to advertise their presence to sperm. Although animals do not appear to have any such mechanism, the jelly-like coating of the sea urchin egg has important functions in promoting fertilization of the egg. It contains a protein known as *fertilizin,* which gradually dissolves in the water. Sperms react to its presence by increased activity. The mitochondria in their mid-sections oxidize sugar at a faster rate, enabling them to swim faster—although still at random. Fertilizin also causes the acrosome to extrude its sperm filament. It is not clear how this increased activity promotes fertilization of the egg, and it may be a by-product of some other process going on within the sperm. In any event, the fertilizin certainly does prolong active life of the sperm.

Fertilizin has other functions as well, for it reacts chemically with a protein that is found in sperm cells, *antifertilizin*. The reaction somehow makes the sperms sticky so that they tend to clump together. The whole reaction is similar to what happens when antibodies in the blood cause invading bacteria, or the wrong kind of blood cells, to clump together. It is the action of fertilizin on the antifertilizin of the sperm that enables the sperm to become attached to the surface of the egg. The reaction is highly specific; that is, fertilizin of a given species reacts only with antifertilizin of the same species. This slight difference between the fertilizins of different species is the most effective barrier to fertilization of a sea urchin egg by a different species. Higher animals often have complex mating processes that perform the same function, and the chemical specificity of their fertilizin is probably not nearly as great.

Once the sperm has touched the surface of the egg, the cytoplasm of the egg surface moves up the sperm filament and spreads out into a broad, funnel-shaped structure (see Figure 6-4) with the wide end surrounding the head of the sperm. This *fertilization cone* engulfs the sperm, and then either the entire sperm or only its head is drawn down into the egg.

Activation of the egg involves a special kind of process known as the *cortical reaction,* which is crucial to all the steps that follow. The outermost layer of the egg, just under the cell membrane, is the *egg cortex.* It contains a large number of tiny granules. When a sperm becomes fastened to the egg surface, the granules at that point burst. This causes the neighboring granules to burst also, releasing their substance into the cytoplasm. The result is a wave of bursting cortical granules that passes over the entire surface of the egg in about twenty seconds. The material released from the granules (possibly antifertilizin, which has been found in eggs) combines with the egg cell membrane, making it harder and more impenetrable. The cell membrane has been converted into a *fertilization membrane,* which now lifts off the surface of the egg by allowing water to pass in and accumulate just below it.

It is possible to stop the cortical reaction when it has reached halfway around the egg by adding nicotine to the water. This produces eggs that are covered half by a fertilization membrane and half by an unchanged egg membrane. If this is done, the half-egg with the fertilization membrane is profoundly different from the other half. Extra sperms may penetrate the egg membrane, but not the fertilization membrane. The two nuclei can move toward each other only in that half of the egg that is surrounded by a fertilization membrane. And the first step in the development of the embryo, cleavage of the egg into two cells, can only occur where the cortical reaction is complete.

Rejection of extra sperms is a most important function of the egg, for any sperm over the normal quota of one per egg will usually result in abnormalities and early death of the embryo. Certainly the fertilization membrane plays an important role in this function, but it cannot be the whole story. It takes several seconds for the cortical reaction to start, and as much as a minute may elapse before the fertilization membrane is completed. Using the mathematics of probability, it can be shown that this period of time is ample to allow a large number of eggs to be doubly fertilized. But they rarely are. By counting the fraction of eggs that become fertilized a second time, it can be shown that the ability of an egg to receive a sperm is reduced by ninety-five per cent in the first two seconds after fertilization. It is still uncertain what produces this *rapid block* of additional fertilizations. Whatever it is, it probably lasts only until the cortical reaction is complete, for an egg in which the cortical reaction has been blocked halfway receives additional sperms freely.

In many animals—frogs, salamanders, reptiles, birds, some molluscs, and insects—there is no rapid block, and many sperms ordinarily enter the egg. Rejection of the secondary sperms occur later, after one sperm nucleus unites with the egg nucleus. Then the extra sperms die, first those near the nucleus and then those further away. The zygote nucleus apparently produces some substance that kills off extra sperms.

Completion of the fertilization process—the union of the two nuclei—is a co-operative effort. The growth of the aster surrounding the sperm nucleus pushes it toward the center of the egg. Meanwhile the egg nucleus is carried by currents in the cytoplasm until it touches one of the rays of the aster, and it then moves down this ray. Near the center of the egg, the two nuclei finally make contact and fuse, completing the process around which the entire complex of sexual reproduction is centered.

From this point on, the two nuclei are one, and the material contributed by both parents is equally important in controlling the development of the embryo. Soon after fertilization, the new nucleus divides into two parts, each an exact replica of the zygote nucleus (see Chapter 9). After the nucleus divides, a new cell membrane grows across the cell between the two daughter nuclei. This splits the zygote into two cells, usually equal in size.

The process of subdivision of the zygote, known as *cleavage,* repeats itself many times until the zygote has been divided into a large number of cells, all with identical nuclei. However, cleavage does not depend on the presence of the nucleus. If the nucleus is removed, the first few cleavages will proceed more or less as usual, provided only that the cortical reaction has been allowed to go to completion. The vital necessity for the presence of the nucleus is felt a little later, for without the nucleus, the cells of the embryo are unable to differentiate into the countless types necessary to perform all the life functions of a multi-cellular organism.

7

The Embryo

"In nature," wrote the great seventeenth-century Dutch naturalist Jan Swammerdam, "there is no generation, but only propagation, the growth of parts. Thus original sin is explained, for all men were contained in the organs of Adam and Eve. When their stock of eggs is finished, the human race will cease to be."

This elegant and pithy statement expressed the theory of *preformation*. It was almost universally believed in those days that all the structures of an adult are already present in the egg, that the conversion of the egg into an adult is merely a process of growth. Swammerdam, a most meticulous anatomist, dissected the pupa of a butterfly and found all the parts of the butterfly already present, awaiting the moment when the pupa case opens and the butterfly stretches its wings for the first time. Others had already found the embryo plant in seeds and the developing chick in a newly laid hen's egg. The great biologist could not have known in his day that a pupa is not an egg, but a dormant larval stage;

that a seed is not an egg, but a dormant embryo; that a newly laid hen's egg has already been developing for several days within its mother. Swammerdam's evidence for preformation seemed good, and the greatest naturalists of the day accepted it. Each egg contained a miniature adult, complete with eggs of its own containing still-smaller adults. Reproduction was simply a process of removing successively smaller boxes from a set of nesting boxes. When the last box was removed and found to contain nothing smaller, life would come to an end.

Theories of Development

The biological discoveries of the sixteenth and seventeenth centuries reinforced the idea of preformation so strongly that no alternative seemed possible. The more man delved into the inner details of the structure and function of living things, the clearer it became that each part of an animal was a part of an interconnected whole, that no organ could maintain its own life any more than a gear could function in the absence of the rest of the clock. How then could any organ develop before the others? The only conceivable situation was that the whole organism existed, complete in all its parts, within the egg.

The discovery of sperms brought with it a new theory of development. At first their significance was unknown; some biologists thought them invaders of body tissues, like organisms found in the mouth. Others reported finding sperms in the sexual secretions of females, and thought them to be the reproductive structures of both sexes. There was even a report of sperms copulating and producing eggs of their own which grew into more sperms! There seems to be no limit to what can be seen when observation is seasoned too liberally with imagination. When the egg of a mammal was finally discovered, the theory was advanced that it was the sperm, not the egg, that carried the preformed embryo, and that the only function of the egg was to provide a cozy place for the growth of this embryo. Various microscopists saw and drew pictures of the "homunculus," the miniature man in a sperm.

For a hundred years gallons of printer's ink were spilled in a fruitless argument over whether the egg or the sperm was the carrier of the preformed embryo. Both sides produced good logic and meaningless sophistry, triumphs of microscopic technique and outrageously inaccurate observation. The champions of the egg finally won with the discovery of parthenogenesis in aphids, the little bugs that attack roses. Surely if an egg can develop into a normal adult without the help of a sperm, then it is the egg that carries the embryo!

But the victory was temporary. Throughout this period a small group of investigators refused to accept the idea of preformation, believing rather that the embryo developed part by part out of an originally formless egg. In the days when biology was becoming a science, this idea of *epigenesis* had to fight an uphill struggle, for epigenesis sounded too much like spontaneous generation. Unless the organs were already there, where did they come from?

The weaknesses within the preformation theory were fatal and eventually led to its overthrow. If each embryo was preformed within all preceding generations, how is it possible to account for the occasional birth of malformed monsters? If either the sperm or the egg contains everything that makes up the eventual adult, why is it that hybrids can have some characteristics of both parents? Where in a lizard shall we look for its preformed second tail, the one it can grow to replace a lost tail? The absurdity of the whole preformation doctrine became apparent when it was calculated that a present-day rabbit, if present within an ancestor of several thousand years ago, must have been smaller than the rabbit in which it existed by a factor of one followed by one hundred thousand zeros!

The final blow that destroyed preformationism was delivered by Caspar Friedrich Wolff. This mild-mannered German professor, working in St. Petersburg, performed experiments that revised all the existing theories of embryology. In 1768 he published a book in which he described the development of the intestine of a chick, starting as a simple fold of tissue. He explained how this fold closes over to become a tube, which then detaches from its parent tissues. It grows larger and forms the elaborate folds and detailed structure that enable it to do its work. Neither in the egg, nor in the sperm, nor even in the early embryo was a chick's intestine to be found.

The flood of research that followed Wolff's discovery killed the preformation theory. From then on it was clear that development is epigenetic, that each individual creates its own structure out of the formless mass of the egg. No understanding of the nature of this process was possible until the research of another fifty years had produced one of the great generalizations of biology: the cell theory. Once it was known that living things are organized aggregates of cells and that each cell can arise only by division of existing cells, embryological research had a firm base. The study of development now concentrated on such problems as how does the single cell of the zygote become the trillions of cells in the adult? What makes the cells differentiate into the many different kinds in the adult? How do the cells of the adult come to be in the right place?

CLEAVAGE

Every newly formed zygote starts, within an hour or so, the tortuous, hazardous, and almost unbelievably complex process of converting itself into an adult. It begins by dividing the single large cell into a number of smaller ones. This happens in a variety of ways, but in most creatures the zygote first subdivides itself into many cells, each with its own nucleus, without any change in its overall shape or form. Before any structures can be made, a supply of cells is needed. This subdivision of the zygote is called *cleavage*.

Shortly after a sea urchin's egg is fertilized, a tiny groove or furrow appears at the upper end of the egg, as shown in Figure 7-1. The groove extends itself until it completely circles the egg, dividing the zygote into two separate cells. The nucleus has meanwhile divided, so that each of the two cells has half the original nucleus. For a half-hour or an hour, the nuclei grow back to full size, and the cells are then ready to divide again. Another furrow appears, again at the upper end of the egg, perpendicular to the first one. This furrow again divides the embryo vertically, forming four cells, all identical to each other. The third cleavage is perpendicular to the other two, along the equator of the embryo, producing an eight-cell stage. Additional cleavages repeatedly subdivide the cells, often unequally, so that the cells are of various sizes. Meanwhile the cells gradually draw away from the center of the embryo, leaving it hollow. This hollow ball of cells, one cell thick and about the same size and shape as the original egg, marks the end of cleavage and is called a "blastula."

FIGURE 7-1. Cleavage of sea urchin egg.

The egg of a frog cannot cleave exactly as the sea urchin's does because of the large amount of yolk concentrated in the lower half of the frog's egg. The yolk is always at the bottom of the frog's egg, because yolk is heavier than the remainder of the egg cytoplasm, causing the egg to rotate until the yolk is lowest. Cleavage (see Figure 7-2) starts at the upper end of the frog's egg (the "animal pole"), where there is least yolk and most chemically active cytoplasm. The first two furrows divide the egg vertically into four equal quarters and meet each other at the bottom or "vegetal pole" of the egg.

The third cleavage occurs above the center of the egg, so that the eight-cell stage consists of four small, chemically active cells on top of four large cells full of yolk. Subsequent cleavages occur faster in the animal hemisphere, so that the eventual blastula contains many tiny cells above and fewer large, yolk-filled cells below. There are also cleavages parallel to the surface of the embryo, so that the blastula is more than one cell thick.

FIGURE 7-2. Cleavage of frog egg.

In the developing egg of a chick, the egg is quite enormous, and the cytoplasm is confined to a tiny speck on one side. Cleavage occurs only in this tiny mass of cytoplasm and never extends to the rest of the egg. The first cleavage furrow starts in the middle of the flat disc of cytoplasm and extends nearly to its edges (Figure 7-3). The second cleavage furrow is perpendicular to the first, forming an X to mark the spot on the egg surface where the embryo is growing. Subsequent cleavages occur both on the surface and below it, and form a disc-shaped blastula containing a tiny

FIGURE 7-3. Cleavage of chick egg.

cavity and separated from the underlying yolk by a thin, single layer of cells.

At the blastula stage, the embryo in some ways resembles a colony of protozoa. The chief difference between a colony of individual cells and a many-celled organism is that the cells of a colony are much alike, while in a many-celled organism there are many kinds of cells, each having its own distinctive structure and performing a special function. The cells, in other words, are *differentiated*. Both the nerve cell, many inches long and specialized for carrying messages, and the ameba-like, white blood cell that scavenges through the body have been derived by repeated division of the same original zygote. Somewhere along the line, cells began to differ from each other until each of your hundred trillion cells emerged in its proper position, and with the correct physical and chemical structure to enable it to do a specific job.

Cleavage by itself produces no differentiation of cells. Nevertheless, the subdivision of the zygote does produce a variety of cells, for not all parts of the original egg are alike. Surely there is a vast difference between the small, active cells of the upper half of a frog blastula and the large, yolk-filled cells of the lower half. Even where there is no visible difference, as in the sea urchin, delicate chemical and metabolic tests have shown that not all of the cells are equivalent. Differentiation starts by a segregation of materials into different cells, and it is the cleavage of the zygote that does the segregating.

The Gastrula

Once cleavage has produced a blastula in which some cells differ from others, these differences can serve as raw materials on which further differentiation can be built. With the formation of the blastula, the simple segregation of parts comes to an end and the development process then enters a new phase. The blastula is the end of cleavage and the springboard to formation of specialized cells and tissues. Different parts of the embryo start to grow at different rates, effecting gross movement of parts. This brings parts of the embryo into new spatial relationships, where the parts can affect each other and control the next stages of development.

The first step is the movement of certain cells of the blastula from the surface to the inside. This happens in many ways, but the end result is that the vegetal part of the blastula comes to occupy a position inside the embryo, while the animal hemisphere grows over the surface until its material covers the entire embryo. The space between these two materials then becomes occupied by a third tissue, formed either from the material along the margin between the blastula hemispheres or from one of the other tissues. This three-layered structure is the *gastrula*. The outer layer of the gastrula, formed from the animal hemisphere of the egg, is the *ectoderm;* the inner layer, formed from the vegetal half, is the *endoderm*; and the *mesoderm* lies between.

A simple method of gastrula formation is found in the primitive chordate *Branchiostoma* (perhaps better known by its old name Amphioxus). The blastula is a hollow ball with walls just one cell thick. It is practically undifferentiated, although the vegetal cells are slightly larger and contain a little more yolk than the animal cells. Careful measurements of the rate of oxygen consumption of the two tissues show that animal cells contain a larger amount of active cytoplasm than the vegetal cells. Soon after the blastula is complete, the animal cells begin to grow rapidly, so that they exert a force on the margins of vegetal tissue. The vegetal tissue is crowded and bulges inward toward the center of the embryo. This continues until the vegetal tissue is inside the ball, surrounded by the rapidly growing animal tissue.

The result is a hollow, two-layered sphere with a hole in it at the point where the ingrowth has occurred. The original vegetal half is now a layer of endoderm; the original animal half is the outer, ectoderm layer; the original marginal tissue is at the lips of the hole. Later, a bit of tissue pinches off from the inner layer to form the mesoderm. The late gastrula stage has all three layers.

With the formation of the gastrula, the basic body plan of nearly all many-celled animals is established. An animal body may be thought of as a tube-within-a-tube, a digestive tract continuous from one end of the body to the other, surrounded by an outer tube that makes up the body wall. The cavity within the endoderm of the gastrula is the cavity of the digestive system. As the organism grows, this primitive gut develops openings at both ends (mouth and anus) and grows to become the variously coiled, folded, and expanded hollow organs of the digestive system, the mouth, throat, esophagus, stomach, and intestines. Later, outpocketings at different points along this tube form the liver and pancreas, the gill cavities of fishes, and the trachea and lungs of land-living animals. All of these organs are lined with endoderm. Since this tissue originates from the yolk-rich vegetal part of the egg, the digestive system contains a supply of food from the very beginning.

The ectoderm, as might be expected, becomes the epidermis of the skin. But a large part of it becomes the nervous system by a process which will be explained below. In be-

tween the epidermis of the skin and the lining of the digestive system lie the lower layers of the skin, the muscular
layers of the stomach and intestines, the blood and bones,
the heart and arteries, the muscles and membranes that
make up the largest part of the body. All of this is the in-
between tissue, the mesoderm that starts so inconspicuously
(in many organisms) as a thin ring of cells along the lips
of the gastrula cavity.

There are endless variations on the process of gastrulation. In the frog, there is so much yolk in the vegetal
hemisphere that it cannot be pushed inward by growth of
animal tissue. Gastrulation begins at the gray crescent (see
Figure 7-4). The shiny, black, animal tissue just above the
gray crescent starts its growth spurt and pushes down over
the gray crescent, until the crescent is forced inward to take
up a position between the outer and inner layers.

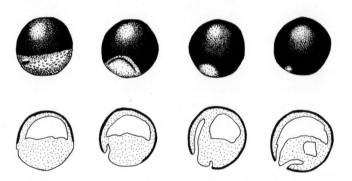

FIGURE 7-4. Gastrulation in frog. (*Top row:*) surface views at
successive stages. (*Bottom row:*) corresponding sections.

Then the black animal tissue alongside the gray crescent also begins to push downward over the vegetal half,
until the region of growth girdles the embryo along the border between the two halves. This growth circle pushes down-

ward, growing smaller as it moves, until the entire embryo is covered with the black animal tissue (now the ectoderm), except for a tiny hole where the white yolk of the vegetal half (now the endoderm) peeks through. The mesoderm is formed partly from the gray crescent tissue and partly from tissue that pushes in from the margins of the opening into the gastrula cavity.

The egg of a chick contains thousands of times as much yolk as that of a frog and millions of times the amount in a *Branchiostoma* egg. When the chick blastula is complete, the yolk, still visible from the surface, instead of occupying a tiny hole takes up almost the entire surface of the egg. The ectoderm cannot grow to cover the whole egg, and the entire gastrula is a tiny spot spread out on the surface of the enormous mass of yolk. For the period of incubation, the yolk is gradually used up as the embryo grows. A day before hatching, there is still a mass of yolk in a sac protruding from a slit in the chick's belly; it is drawn in and the slit closes up shortly before hatching.

Organ Formation

By whatever process the gastrula forms, it is a critical stage in the life of the embryo. The movement of tissues has created an overall structural plan. From this point on, the details of the structure are worked out, at first roughly and then in greater detail. The whole process is like an artist painting a picture. First he blocks in the main areas, then he sketches in shapes of the objects, and finally he meticulously adds detail. The gastrula is the roughest sketch, the main outline of the finished picture.

The finer details are not added all at once, but in a rigid sequence. The first region to be sketched is the nervous system. This originates, shortly after the gastrula is complete, as a thickened layer of ectoderm that extends down the back of the embryo (Figure 7-5). In the frog, as in most other vertebrates, this thickened layer sinks down below the level of the surrounding tissue to form a groove which deepens and lengthens itself toward the tail until it occupies the center of the entire back. When the groove is quite deep, its margins grow toward each other until they meet along the mid-line. Here they unite, starting at the head end, as though someone drew a zipper from the head right down to the end of the tail. This converts the groove into a tube, which now separates from the overlying ectoderm.

FIGURE 7-5. Formation of neural tube of frog.

This tube will eventually become most of the nervous system. By the time it is formed, the digestive and skeletal systems have also begun to differentiate. Let us ignore these other systems and see what happens to the nerve tube. Figure 7-6 shows successive stages in the history of the upper end of this tube in the human embryo. Some parts grow more rapidly and others more slowly, causing the tube to swell in some regions, to bend to fit the available space, to take on a definite detailed structure.

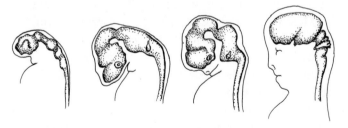

FIGURE 7-6. Differentiation of human brain.

The sketch emerges in greater detail as time proceeds, until a more or less uniform tube has been converted into a highly differentiated brain. What the figure does not show is that differentiation is going on at the microscopic level as well. Cells take up particular positions and grow in special ways to set up the structure of the adult brain, correct down to the minutest details of structure. The process of drawing in details is carried several orders of magnitude beyond what an artist could do. Outgrowths from the brain and the rest of the tube (the spinal cord) eventually reach into all parts of the body to form nearly the whole nervous system.

All systems form by this kind of process, which sometimes reaches fantastic degrees of complexity. In many cases, organs form from a combination of tissues of different origins. The pituitary gland, for example, develops from a bit of nervous tissue growing down from the base of the brain and another tiny piece that meets it by growing up from the roof of the mouth. An eye develops from a part of the brain that grows outward toward the surface, and from the tissues of the skin where the nerve tissue reaches it. The digestive system is at first a tube consisting of an inner layer of endoderm (the original gastrula cavity) covered by a layer of mesoderm. This differentiates into throat, esophagus, stomach, and intestines. In time, cell differences in the walls fill in structural details like gastric glands and villi. Meanwhile, outpocketings grow larger to form the liver, pancreas, trachea, lungs (in land animals), and gill pouches.

One remarkable process is an actual migration of separated cells. Certain cells will separate from a particular position and move precisely to some other position, apparently under their own power. In the new position, they contribute to the formation of an organ. The vertebrae (segments of the back bone) start this way, from cells that wander in from the mesoderm and form a sheath around the primordial cartilaginous backbone.

In the end, all the organs have formed in proper relationship to each other and with their correct detailed internal structure. As if this were not remarkable enough, there is a large margin for error. An embryo will tolerate much insult, and still manage to regroup its parts to produce a normal adult. Experimental embryologists cut out pieces and add bits and very often find that it does not seem to matter. This forms the main weapon for investigation of the mechanisms that control development of the embryo and we will hear more of it in the next section.

DIFFERENTIATION

Biologists refer to this elaboration of detailed structure as *differentiation*. It means nothing more complicated than the process of becoming different. From a fairly uniform zygote emerges a structure whose complexity defies understanding, and we would like to know how this happens. Historically, the first task in studying the emergence of structure was a physical description. What tissues move where and what changes do they undergo to become part of the adult? These are difficult questions, for every part of the embryo is constantly changing, and only the grossest structures can be made out while the animal is alive.

For detailed studies, it is necessary to kill the embryo and slice it into thin sections, so that it can be studied under a high-power microscope. Some tissues grow much faster than others, so that a tissue that makes up half the blastula might become only five per cent of the adult. One of the best methods of studying this problem is to put tiny spots of harmless dye on the embryo and then wait before killing and slicing it for study. The dyes can be found under the microscope, marking the present location of a tissue that was selected and labeled at an earlier stage. In this way it has been found, for example, that most of the vegetal half of the frog blastula becomes the digestive system of the adult, while the animal half becomes mainly epidermis and nervous system. The gray crescent is transformed largely into the *notochord,* a stiff cartilaginous rod that forms the only backbone of a young tadpole. It is replaced by the bony, vertebral column when the tadpole turns into a frog.

Once something was known about the normal developmental path of the main tissues of the embryo, experiments were begun to find out why tissues develop as they do. The chief weapon of the experimental embryologist in this struggle has been the transplantation of tissue—moving bits of tissue from place to place within the embryo, or from older to younger embryos, or even to embryos of different species. If a piece of presumptive epidermis—tissue known to grow into a part of the epidermis in the normal course of events —is stained and then removed from its place in the animal half of the frog blastula, it can later be found at any desired time, regardless of how it may have changed. In many species, if the transplant is made in the blastula stage, the nature of the tissue can be changed, almost without limit. The tissue will convert itself into the type appropriate to its new location rather than the kind it would have become if it had not been moved. We say that the embryo *self-regulates;* that is, it can grow into a normal adult even if it has to change the fate of some of its tissues to do so. Presumptive epidermis has been made to grow into spinal cord, muscle, kidney, intestinal wall, and other tissues. At the blastula stage, nearly any tissue can be caused to grow into any part of the adult. Its ultimate fate depends on its location within the embryo, not on any intrinsic property of its own.

The wide range of potentialities that tissues have at first is gradually restricted as the tissues age. If presumptive epidermis is transplanted at a later stage, after the main body tissues have started to differentiate (the gastrula stage) the results are different. The presumptive epidermis will become epidermis wherever it is placed—in the spinal cord, or the intestine, or the kidneys. Some change has taken place in its internal structure, a change that has set it irreversibly on the road to differentiation as epidermis. We say that the tissue has been *determined*. In the entire lexicon of biology no other word conceals as great a depth of ignorance. The nature of the determination of tissue has eluded experimenters since it was first discovered fifty years ago.

Determination does not occur at once, but rather produces a progressive narrowing of the potentialities of a tissue. A piece of presumptive belly epidermis at first can be changed into any tissue at all; a little later it can no longer become intestine or kidney, but can still be converted into nerve tissue or any part of the skin; still later, it can become only epidermis. If the transplant is done at a later stage, determination is found to be complete. Presumptive belly epidermis cannot even be changed into head epidermis, and the attempt results in an adult frog with an incongruous piece of white belly skin on his head.

Just what happens when a tissue irreversibly differentiates is still an open question. There have been several theories about the nature of the process, which are discussed in Chapter 8. Actually, there can be little hope of understanding what is going on until we know more about the chemistry of the cell, for determination is probably first and foremost a chemical process. As you read further, you will see that there are certain highly suggestive clues, but as yet no firm answers.

REGENERATION

Typically, a fully differentiated cell can no longer change itself into anything else, according to most biologists. But is this transformation really permanent? There is now considerable evidence that, at least in some cases, specialization is reversible. The evidence has come from intensive studies of regeneration. All living things have the ability to recover from injury, and this capacity to regenerate has lately been used to gain insight into the similar processes that go on in a developing embryo.

You learned the first time you put on roller skates that a skinned knee repairs itself in a few days. Perhaps you have discovered a little about the ability of broken bones to knit. You also know the limits of your regenerative capacity, that a fingernail will grow back, but not a finger. You have unseen regenerative powers of which you are normally not aware. The outer layer of your skin wears off continually and is replaced by new growth from underneath. A biologist may remove three-fourths of a rat's liver and find it grown back to full size a few weeks later. We can only wonder why this same capacity for repair does not extend to a lung or a leg.

In many creatures it does. A salamander can grow a new leg as easily as you repair a cut finger. A starfish can be cut into five equal sections, and each will grow into a normal, full-sized animal. Many of the lower animals—worms, polyps, protozoa, sponges—and even the most complex plants can regenerate the adult from small pieces, as every gardener knows. But not the best botanist knows why the rose leaf will never grow roots the way an African violet does, or why a piece of stem of a willow tree will take root while peach trees can be grown only from seed.

Regenerative ability is often a function of age. If a leg

is removed from a tadpole soon after it forms, a whole new leg can grow, and the tadpole becomes a normal frog. If the amputation is done slightly later, a forelimb can be regenerated, but not a hind limb, and after that, no limb can be replaced. Comparable changes are found in people. A broken bone knits much faster in a child than in an adult, while it may not heal at all in a very old man. In the very earliest stages, up to a few days after fertilization of the egg, two frogs can be produced by separation of a single embryo into halves. This self-regulation process, regeneration in its most extreme form, also occurs in human beings when a single embryo divides to produce identical twins. There are several well-known cases in which a human embryo divided to form five separate individuals. At this stage, our regenerative ability is not inferior to that of the starfish.

The champion regenerator is the little freshwater polyp *Hydra*. This tiny creature can be chopped into hundreds of fragments, and each piece will round up into a little ball and then rearrange its cells into the normal tubular shape of the adult. Tentacles grow at the upper end, a fleshy "foot" forms at the bottom, and the creature is back in business. But even here tissues do not become completely undifferentiated while regeneration is going on. The adult body of a *Hydra* consists of two concentric tubes, each one cell thick. The inner tube is the endoderm and has mainly a digestive function, just like the endoderm of higher animals. The outer layer of cells, the ectoderm, performs most other vital functions. It does not appear to be possible to convert endoderm to ectoderm or vice versa; a complete *Hydra* can grow from a fragment only if both kinds of tissue are present.

Many worms, such as the earthworm or the aquatic flatworm *Planaria*, can be cut in half to produce two new individuals, but cannot regenerate from fragments like a *Hydra*. If an earthworm is cut in half, the reorganization of tissue occurs only at the cut surface. At this point there is a breakdown of the structure of the tissue, and a formation of an undifferentiated mass of embryonic tissue known as a "blastema." This blastema seems to form by *dedifferentiation,* conversion of specialized tissues of the cut surface into embryonic tissue. It then redifferentiates into the specialized tissues of the missing half-worm. Dedifferentiation and reorganization are localized in the blastema rather than involving the entire body as they do in a *Hydra* fragment.

We must be cautious in assuming that there is a complete reversal of differentiation, for it is possible that the cells of the blastema, in spite of their embryonic appearance, really consist of several types. Perhaps these cells consist of potential muscle derived from muscle, potential nerve derived from nerve, and so on, just as the *Hydra* fragment must consist of ectoderm and endoderm if regeneration is to occur.

This question has been studied most exhaustively in the salamander, in which an amputated leg can regenerate fully. Immediately after amputation, a blood clot forms, and the epidermis (outer layer of the skin) adjacent to the wound begins to move in and cover the wound surface. After a few hours, the wound is completely covered by epidermis, and then the epidermal cells begin to reproduce until the skin has become quite thick. Meanwhile, the cut ends of the nerves grow outward toward the epidermis until large numbers of branch nerves have penetrated into and even through the epidermis. This is quite unexpected, because normal epidermis has very little nerve supply.

A third process is also occurring: the blood vessels, bones, cartilage, muscle, connective tissues, and other tissues of the stump dedifferentiate and lose their structure, gradually being converted into a formless mass. Cells from this dissociating tissue migrate outward to a position just under the epidermis to form a blastema of tissue that is, to all appearances, embryonic. After several days, cells in the stump divide to form new cells, which migrate into the blastema. Then the blastema cells start to divide, and within three weeks the blastema begins to differentiate into the tissues that will form a new leg.

THEORIES OF REGENERATION

At first glance, this seems to be a true case of dedifferentiation, of mature tissues regaining their embryonic character. In fact, there are three different hypotheses that have been advanced to explain the formation and subsequent history of the blastema: (1) The obvious possibility is that there is reversion to embryonic form and then redifferentiation of the tissue. (2) The dedifferentiation is only apparent, for the blastema cells, although superficially alike, might possess only the potentialities of the tissue from which they arose, so that bone gives rise only to bone and muscle to muscle. (3) The blastema might arise not from the mature tissues of the stump, but from permanently embryonic cells, specially reserved for the purpose in the connective tissues or brought to the site by the blood.

The third alternative can almost certainly be ruled out, although it was the most popular choice ten years ago. Exposure to X-rays destroys the ability of a leg to regenerate. If the entire body of a salamander except the leg is X-rayed, a new leg can still grow after amputation. This clearly implies that regeneration is accomplished locally with no help from the rest of the body. It is true that there are embryonic cells in the connective tissue, but their number is too small to account for the blastema. It has recently been found that there is practically no cell division during the four days when the blastema is forming. The differentiated stump tissues are the only possible source of the blastema.

A theory popular until recently was that the blastema forms chiefly from the epidermis that spreads out to cover the wound. No regeneration occurs if the epidermis is removed, but transplanted epidermis is completely effective in doing whatever it is that the epidermis does to promote blastema formation. Whole skin will not do; the blastema will not form if the lower layers of the skin are allowed to come between the stump and the epidermis. However, if the blastema is labelled with radioactive iodine, it is found that the movement of material is outward from the blastema into the epidermis rather than the other way round. Whatever its function, the epidermis does not substantially contribute to the blastema.

This leaves only the stump tissues as a source for the blastema. We would still like to know whether the cells of the blastema are really all alike, or whether they retain their specific potentialities while in the apparently embryonic form. As long ago as 1925, an experiment was performed which seemed to answer this question. The humerus, or upper arm bone, of a newt was removed, leaving the rest of the foreleg, including the soft tissues of the upper arm, intact. After healing, the foreleg was amputated through the middle of the boneless upper part (see Figure 7-7). When the limb regenerated, it contained a normal lower half, complete with all the bones of the lower forelimb and foot. Even the lower half of the humerus was formed, although the upper half was still lacking. It seemed clear that the bone in the newly regenerated part of the limb was formed from some other kind of tissue. It certainly looked like a case of redifferentiation.

Some recent experiments have cast a doubt on this conclusion. Careful counts were made of the numbers of different kinds of cells in the stump, the rates of division of

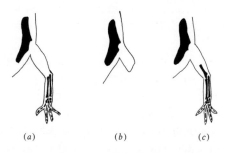

(a)   *(b)*   *(c)*

FIGURE 7-7. Regeneration of boneless newt foreleg: (*a*) foreleg with humerus removed; (*b*) amputation through center of boneless upper foreleg; (*c*) regenerated limb.

the different kinds of cells of the stump, the rates of division of the redifferentiating cells in the blastema, and the numbers of different kinds of cells in the regenerated limb. All of these ratios were in agreement for any particular kind of tissue; if, say, 10 per cent of the stump consisted of cartilage cells, then 10 per cent of the blastema produced cartilage in the regenerated limb. This is strong evidence that regenerated tissues are produced from similar tissues of the stump, that the dedifferentiation is only apparent and the tissues retain their specificity during their seemingly embryonic stage in the blastema.

If this is so, some way must be found to account for the formation of bone in a regenerated limb formed from a boneless stump. It is likely that this dilemma will be resolved within a few years, but at present we still do not know whether a completely differentiated tissue cell can turn into something entirely different. We know from studies of embryos that the ultimate fate of a cell is sealed while the physical structure of the cell is still embryonic, and the same sort of thing may be happening in a blastema. And we still have no idea what makes a cell whose future is rigidly determined different from one which still has many paths open to it.

Ever since the earliest studies on regeneration, men have wondered why the salamander is so much more fortunate than we. A man who loses so much as the tip of a finger must plan the rest of his life without that fingertip. Why can a salamander regrow a whole leg? If we ever find out, can we use the knowledge to enable people to do the same?

If the answer is ever found, there is little doubt that the nerves will enter into it somehow. If nerves are cut back when the leg of a salamander is removed, the skin will heal over the wound, but no blastema will form, and very little breakdown of the stump tissue will occur. Until the blastema is well developed, its growth can be stopped instantly by removing the nerves, although a mature blastema can grow into a complete leg in the absence of nerves. Further, a wound in the skin near the leg can be made to form a blastema and grow into an extra leg merely by rerouting a nerve in the wound area. Perhaps the nerves serve as a pathway for the migration of special cells or for the flow of some special chemical. Or perhaps the nerve sheaths themselves contribute to the blastema.

One experiment, and so far one only, indicates that the loss of the capacity to form a blastema is not necessarily irreversible. An adult frog cannot normally regenerate a leg. But if the stump is repeatedly irritated by pricking it with a needle, it will form a blastema and grow a fully normal, new leg. Surely we may hope that a way will be found to accomplish this in man.

8

The Control of Development

Experimental embryology is a twentieth-century science, concerning itself with the investigation of the mechanisms by which an egg converts itself into an adult. We see that as the embryo grows, its parts differentiate in just the right way to produce a functioning adult, and we wonder at the exactness with which differentiation occurs. We discover an astonishing degree of self-regulation, so that proper differentiation occurs even if the embryo is grossly damaged. We find exact limits to self-regulation, for tissues soon or late become determined and can no longer adapt their development to the tissue environment.

The earliest theory of differentiation, popular at the end of the last century, held that the nucleus controls all the growth and development of each cell of the embryo. The nucleus was supposed to contain "determinants," materials that could control the differentiation of cells. It was supposed that determinants are sorted among the cells at each cell division, and that the ultimate form of the cell depended on which determinants it received. The function of the cytoplasm was to respond to the determinants in the nucleus by growing into, say, a nerve cell or a muscle cell. Some of the first experiments in the field of embryology were done to test this theory, and they seemed to confirm it. If one cell of the two-cell stage of a frog embryo is destroyed by piercing it with a hot needle, the other cell develops into a half-tadpole, just as if it contained determinants for only half a body.

THE BEGINNING OF DIFFERENTIATION

Later experiments were not so kind to the theory of determinants. If the two cells of the frog embryo are carefully separated instead of being kept together with one cell dead, both cells will develop into normal tadpoles and then normal adults. At this stage, the capacity for self-regulation is astonishing. Any self-regulation is a mortal blow to the theory of determinants, for it shows that a cell can still develop in any of a variety of ways after it has been left with only a small part of the original nuclear material.

One of the classic experiments in the investigation of differentiation was done by Hans Spemann in 1928. He tied a hair in a loop around a newly fertilized newt's egg (Figure 8-1) and squeezed the egg almost in half, but left the two halves connected by a narrow bridge. The half with the nucleus cleaved four times, forming sixteen cells, and one of the nuclei than crossed over the bridge into the other half. Spemann then separated the two halves. According to the determinant theory, one half of the egg contained one-sixteenth of the determinants and the other half had fifteen-sixteenths of them. But the half-egg with the single nucleus then started to cleave, and eventually grew into a perfectly normal adult. That single nucleus, formed as the end product of four divisions of the zygote nucleus, was just as effective as the original zygote nucleus in performing its mysterious functions. Spemann suggested that all nuclei are completely equivalent, that there is no segregation of determinants when cells divide.

FIGURE 8-1. Constriction of a newt egg: (*a*) constriction; (*b*) after several cleavages; (*c*) a nucleus enters the undivided part; (*d*) the halves are separated.

Spemann's conclusion has been spectacularly confirmed by a more recent experiment. A frog's egg is pricked with a needle to cause it to start developing parthenogenetically, and its nucleus is then removed. The zygote is then supplied with a different nucleus, taken from a later embryo of, perhaps, one hundred thousand cells. There are great surgical difficulties in this operation, but zygotes treated in this way have been raised to normal adulthood. As little as one-one hundred thousandth of the original nucleus, it seems, has all the properties of the original zygote nucleus. The theory of determinants could not survive this crucial test, and we now realize that in the early embryo at least, all nuclei are equivalent, that each half-nucleus at the end of a division of a cell must grow back into a complete nucleus before the cell can divide again.

Once it was established that all nuclei are equivalent, clues to the cause of differentiation were sought in the cytoplasm. If the four cells resulting from the second cleavage of a sea urchin egg are separated from each other, each can self-regulate to become a complete small larva and ultimately a complete adult. But let us wait a half-hour, until the third cleavage has divided the embryo equatorially into eight cells. In order for a complete embryo to form, at least two cells are now needed, one from the animal hemisphere and one from the vegetal half. If the embryo is divided along the equatorial cleavage plane, the animal half develops into a larva consisting mainly of skin and nerves, while the vegetal half becomes a large digestive tract with little skin and no nerves. The process of cleavage has produced differentiation because the egg *cytoplasm* is not really homogeneous.

The same phenomena are seen in the egg of a frog. The animal half of a frog's egg is covered with a shiny, black pigment, while the vegetal half is nearly white, as it contains large amounts of yolk and no pigment. When the egg is fertilized, the black hemispherical cap shifts its position away from the point at which the sperm entered, so that a small strip of the deep animal cytoplasm is visible through the surface of the egg. This strip is called the *gray crescent,* and it eventually serves a most important function in the differentiation of the embryo. Even after many cells have formed, it is still possible to divide the embryo into two parts, both of which will develop, provided that the division is done vertically through the gray crescent. But a half-embryo that does not include half of the gray crescent will be unable to self-regulate, and converts itself into a miscellaneous collection of disorganized tissues. Once again we find that differentiation exists in the egg long before cleavage begins.

The zygote nucleus appears to have remarkably little to do with the cleavage process. The zygote nucleus of a salamander has been replaced with one from a different species which cleaves somewhat differently, and the pattern of cleavage follows that of the cytoplasm, not the nucleus.

Some activated eggs can cleave even if the nucleus is removed altogether, although the embryo dies in the blastula stage. Differentiation of cells begins by sorting not nuclear determinants, but components of the cytoplasm into different cells during the cleavage process.

This is only the beginning. Differentiation is a process that works itself out in greater and greater detail as development proceeds. What determines whether a given cell turns into a skin cell or a muscle fiber? And what role does the nucleus play in the process?

EMBRYONIC INDUCTION

Although the nature of determination is still largely unknown, quite a lot is known about the processes that bring it about. The events that lead up to the differentiation of the parts of the eye have been studied in great detail. In the early human embryo, the brain can be seen clearly as a thick-walled hollow structure that occupies most of the head. From the sides of this brain, two tubes grow out laterally toward the sides of the head. When they reach the skin, the ends of the tube flatten out and bulge inward to form a hollow, double-walled structure called the *optic cup* (Figure 8-2), which is connected to the brain by a stalk formed of the original tube. The inner wall of the optic cup becomes the retina of the eye. In it will form nerve cells that grow back along the stalk to the brain, forming the optic nerve. The lip of the cup becomes thin, flat, and pigmented to produce the iris with its muscles. The opening at the mouth of the cup becomes the pupil of the eye.

The optic cup has many of the properties of the whole embryo. Experiments with frog embryos have shown that it can regulate itself over a wide range, so that if an early optic cup is split in half and one-half transplanted to the tail, two complete eyes will form. The tadpole with the

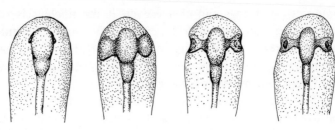

FIGURE 8-2. Development of the optic cup and lens in the human embryo.

extra eye does not, however, have a useful additional way of telling where he has been, for the extra eye can form no nervous connections with the brain. The eye cup has already begun to differentiate into an eye, and is therefore already determined to become an eye, but the separate *parts* of the eye are not yet determined, so self-regulation occurs. At a later stage, it becomes impossible to make two eyes out of one.

Retina and iris are only two parts of the completed eye. The lens, cornea, and the hard coats that protect the eyeball are formed from the epidermis where the eyecup comes into contact with it. When the optic cup reaches the epidermis, the skin tissue begins to thicken and eventually becomes a lens. Later, the adjacent epidermis forms the cornea and protective coats. The crucial fact is that the *same sequence of events occurs in the tail* where the transplanted optic cup touches the epidermis! It is clear that contact with the optic cup causes the epidermis to undergo the changes that convert it into a lens. Later, contact with the lens and eyeball causes the changes in the adjacent epidermis that convert them into the other parts of the eye.

Here is the vital clue to the ability of an embryo to organize itself into a coherent, functioning whole. Tissues develop in their correct relationship to each other because (in part at least) a differentiated tissue has the power to control the development of other tissues with which it comes into contact. However determination occurs, there can be no doubt that the direction of determination is controlled by adjacent tissues a little further along in their development. Once its future has been determined, the second tissue differentiates, and in doing so affects the determination of still other tissues. Step by step, the eye is built into a functioning organ, with all its parts in their correct places. By this process, the whole embryo with its countless specialized cells is made from the nearly uniform cells of the blastula. This process, by which a tissue gives developmental cues to its neighbors, is called "embryonic induction," and is the chief mechanism of the organization of the embryo.

When embryonic induction was discovered, there were two hypotheses as to its nature: that the inducing tissue stimulates its neighbors either by physical contact or by chemical secretion. Physical contact was quickly ruled out, since an extract of the inducing tissue was just as effective as the intact cells. The next research steps were inevitable. What chemicals, specifically, produce the phenomenon of induction? Answers to this question were not long in coming, but unfortunately there were too many answers! Literally dozens of different materials—proteins, nucleic acids, steroids, fatty acids, etc.—have by now been shown to be capable of causing a particular form of differentiation of tissue.

After thirty years of painstaking investigation, a single natural inducing agent has finally been isolated. It has been found that an extract of the ventral half of the spinal cord of a chick will, if injected into a chick cell-tissue culture, cause the adjacent tissue to differentiate into cartilage. In the normal development of the chick, the cartilages of the vertebral column form first just below the spinal cord, so it is clear that the spinal cord induces cartilage formation. The thirty years of searching now seem to be on the verge of bearing fruit. By the time you read this, it is probable that the exact chemical nature of a specific inducing agent will be known.

There must be inducing agents without end in a developing embryo, but if we had our choice, there is one in particular we would like to have. In the frog gastrula, there is a bit of tissue just under the ectoderm at the upper end of the back. It will, in the normal course of events, become the notochord of the tadpole. It was the gray crescent of the egg and blastula. It is one of the most active tissues of the blastula and is the first tissue to be tucked inside the embryo when the rapid growth of the animal-hemisphere ectoderm begins to turn the blastula into a gastrula. As gastrulation continues, this piece of tissue moves in, up, and forward, nearly to the front of the embryo.

If a bit of this tissue is removed and implanted under the ectoderm of another gastrula, a neural groove will form above it. The embryo will also form its own neural groove in the usual position, so that the embryo will have two. Each neural groove then organizes the tissue around it, so that two more or less complete embryos will form. In this way, it is possible to produce twins, or tadpoles with two heads or two tails. This bit of mesoderm tissue starts off a series of inductions that results in complete differentiation of all tissues, and it is therefore called the "primary organizer" of the embryo.

The nature of the primary organizer is just as mysterious as that of other inducing agents. It works when dead just as well as when alive; chemical extracts also work, as do a wide variety of laboratory chemicals such as certain steroids, special proteins, and nucleic acids. At a later stage, the primary organizer, now partially differentiated into notochord, induces the formation of other tissues of the back, such as muscles and the cartilages that eventually form the vertebrae. It is unlikely that the same chemical is involved in all cases, and the only real clue to the nature of the organizing chemicals is the recent discovery that the inducing agent for cartilage appears to be a nucleic acid.

The Responding Tissue

It must not be imagined that the elusive inducing agents carry specific instructions for differentiation which will work the same way in any cell. Transplantation experiments have shown that in many species all cells have the potentialities, at first, of developing into any kind of adult cell. The induction process is a method of determining *which* of the many possible kinds of growth patterns a particular tissue will follow. As the tissue grows older, its range of possible fates decreases, and it therefore cannot respond to inducing agents as it did in its youth. The eyecup, for example, will organize a lens only when it comes into contact with tissue capable of responding appropriately. Induction is a two-way process, involving a specific inducing tissue and a tissue *competent* to respond. Any ectoderm is at first competent to form lens, but later, lens-competence is restricted more and more. Eventually, only the ectoderm at the sides of the head has the competence to become lens tissue, and may do so even in the absence of any induction.

Changing competence is simply one more mystery, as it is not at all understood. There has lately been some support for an old idea that might be able to unite all these troublesome ideas into one unified theory. This is the concept of *specific inhibition,* the idea that as a tissue differentiates, it produces special chemicals that pass into neighboring cells and *prevent* them from undergoing the same kind of differentiation. This could account, for example, for the clear limitation of the size of a lens. As epidermis changed to lens, it would produce metabolic products different from those of the rest of the epidermis. These special chemicals then might pass into the neighboring cells and prevent them from following the path that leads to lens tissue, so that they necessarily undergo another kind of differentiation.

There is now considerable evidence that some such process actually occurs. If the egg of a frog is grown in a medium containing pieces of adult heart, the embryo will fail to develop a heart. Similarly the presence of a brain prevents the brain from forming, and blood in the culture medium inhibits blood formation. Similar experiments have been done on developing chick embryos, using cell-free extracts of various organs rather than the whole organ, with the same results.

The notochord of a frog (the primordial, cartilaginous backbone) serves as organizer of the adjacent tissue, causing the cells alongside it to differentiate into the muscles of the back. But if the notochord is removed, some of this adjacent tissue moves into the wound and reorganizes itself into a new notochord. It seems as though the most active tissue differentiates first and turns into notochord. Any tissue has the potentiality of becoming notochord, but the neighboring material never gets that far normally because it is affected by products of the tissue that is already turning into notochord; therefore, it takes a different path and becomes muscle. Presumably, it then produces a different set of chemical products, which prevent the next tissue from becoming muscle, causing it to turn into something else.

In one group of experiments published in 1961, fine details of this process as it controls the differentiation of parts of the chick nervous system have been worked out.

The nervous system normally begins as a narrow groove down the center of the back, which closes over to form a tube. The front end of this tube is the most active part and starts its differentiation first. It becomes the forebrain, and successive parts of the tube, from the front and moving rearward, turn into midbrain, hindbrain, and spinal cord. If macerated forebrain from a later embryo is injected, the forebrain degenerates and the rest of the nervous system is left unaffected. If midbrain material is injected, the forebrain and midbrain are damaged, while the rest of the tube develops normally.

Macerated spinal cord will inhibit the entire brain. Each part of the brain produces materials that inhibit its own development and also the formation of any part further forward, but do not affect what happens further to the rear. Probably any part of the tube is a potential forebrain, but the most active part, at the front of the tube, gets to the forebrain stage first and prevents its neighboring tissue from becoming forebrain. The next tissue, unable to become forebrain, becomes midbrain and inhibits, in turn, its rearward neighbor, until the entire nervous system has acquired its correct differentiation.

There is a kind of excitement in the air when a new idea seems to be on the verge of producing momentous discoveries. This excitement now surrounds the laboratories that are investigating specific inhibition. Some scientists believe that it is here that the long-sought key to the mystery of embryonic induction is to be found. This may be true, although it is difficult at present to imagine how specific inhibition could account for the induction of, say, lens by a completely different tissue that moves in from some other part of the body. It seems likely that the search for the specific inducing agents will continue.

THE WORK OF THE NUCLEUS

After all the modern work in experimental embryology, we seem to have come back to a kind of preformation idea. There is a preformed structure in the egg, but it is not the adult structure. It is a pattern of development which can go to a successful conclusion even if disrupted. Organization and differentiation are cytoplasmic events, but they can occur only if there is a nucleus. Without it, the embryo cleaves a few times and degenerates into a formless mass. What part does the nucleus play?

To answer this question, we must first find some way to separate the effects of the nucleus from those of the cytoplasm. Experiments in which the nucleus is transplanted can do this for us, but this method is very difficult, often fails, and is limited to embryos in which operations of this kind can be performed. Nature provides us with a much more useful method, for the sperm contributes as much nucleus as the egg, but practically no cytoplasm. One such experiment has been done by crossing two varieties of rabbit, the Polish and the Flemish Giant, which is almost three times the weight of the Polish rabbit when fully grown. Two Polish rabbits will invariably have Polish young, but if the father is a purebred Flemish Giant, the young rabbits will become Giants even if the mother is of the Polish type.

If you know a little genetics, you will recognize this situation: the Flemish Giant character is dominant. Since the father contributed nothing but a single sperm nucleus to his progeny, and since the eggs were all alike, the difference between a Flemish Giant rabbit and a Polish rabbit must be caused by the nucleus, not the egg cytoplasm. Both nuclei are equivalent; an egg nucleus of the Flemish Giant type and a sperm nucleus of the Polish type will also produce Giant offspring.

The difference between these two types of rabbit can be recognized as early as the cleavage stage. An embryo destined to become a Giant cleaves at a faster rate and therefore produces a blastula with more cells. Somehow or other the nucleus of the zygote has speeded up the rate of cleavage, and the long development process eventually makes a big bunny.

This is an unusual case, for the nucleus does not generally have much effect on the process of cleavage. It is usually in the later stages, after gastrulation, that the effects of the nucleus become manifest. There is, for example, a type of mouse that has a nuclear defect. If both egg and sperm have the same defect, the embryos die at an early stage. The embryos appear to be perfectly normal up to the gastrula stage, but the notochord never differentiates. Since this differentiation is necessary for induction of later processes, the embryo becomes disorganized and falls apart.

It seems to be common for the effects of a defective nucleus to be expressed at a particular stage and in a particular organ. In another type of mouse, the young are born perfectly normal but do not develop the sense of vision about two weeks after birth as normal mice do. The first sign of the defect can be found five days after the mouse is born, for at that time it can be seen that the normal differentiation of the cells of the retina does not occur. It seems reasonable to assume that the normal differentiation of the retina cells requires the participation of the nucleus in some process that occurs within the first few days after birth.

Localized nuclear effects can sometimes produce large-scale changes in the animal. A breed of dwarf mice is known in which the embryos grow normally until most of the organs have at least begun to differentiate, which takes about a week. But one organ fails to develop properly: the pituitary gland. This gland, located at the base of the brain, normally produces a hormone that circulates in the blood and stimulates the growth of the whole body. In dwarf mice, the pituitary gland lacks certain crucial cells and the mice are less than half normal size when fully grown. They can be made to grow to normal size by injections of the pituitary growth hormone. One early effect of the nucleus is in the development of a single organ, but the secondary effects change the entire body.

There are other cases of this kind; in one breed of mice, the young live only a few weeks because of widespread deficiencies in the skeleton. It is found that the process of dissolving and reabsorbing of bone, which is necessary for new bone growth to occur, cannot take place. Since this process is controlled by a hormone produced in the parathyroid gland, it is possible that we again have a localized nuclear effect that produces widespread changes in the body.

Hormones can affect the entire body because they circulate in the blood. But there is a more basic phenomenon by which one tissue controls another. This is embryonic induction, in which the development of any given tissue depends on the previous normal growth of neighboring tissues. There is no shortage of cases in which a nuclear defect causes abnormal growth of a single tissue, which then produces widespread abnormality and death because induction cannot take place in the normal way.

In one breed of mouse, a defective nucleus fails to produce sufficient growth of the *ureters*. These tubes, which carry urine from the kidneys to the bladder, ordinarily grow upward from a place near the base of the spine and induce the formation of kidney tubules at their upper ends. In the defective mice, the ureters never reach the competent tissue at their upper ends, so that no kidney tubules form. The result is that the mice form no kidneys and die of an accumulation of urea.

In one well-known case, it is the primary head-organizer that is defective. This occurs in a breed of guinea pigs in which some of the babies are born with the head too narrow, and the eyes, ears, and other organs of the two sides fused together in the middle. In extreme cases, no head forms at all! Exactly similar defects can be produced in frogs and salamanders by removing part of the primary organizer. The head part of the primary organizer of the guinea pigs seems to be lacking or defective, while the spinal cord part functions normally.

One interesting case illustrates the effect of the nucleus in later stages of induction. Two closely related species of toads differ in that one of them forms two pairs of gills in the tadpole stage, while the other forms three. Gill formation is induced by the underlying tissue of the mouth. Breeding experiments show that the number of gills depends on the nucleus. If epidermis is transplanted from one species to another in the appropriate region, the number of gills formed depends on the *host* species; that is, epidermis that would normally form two gills can be made to form three by exposing it to a different inducing situation. The three-gill epidermis can also be made to develop only two by transplanting. Furthermore, transplantation of the *mouth* tissue from one species to another can change the number of gills. Clearly, the epidermis can grow either way, and the mouth tissue supplies the stimulus either for two gills or three. The nucleus has controlled, as far as we can tell, only the kind of induction that takes place.

In some cases, the nucleus controls not the inducing agents, but the ability of the tissue to respond to them. Some species of salamander larvae have a pair of tentacle-like structures on the side of the head, just behind the mouth. These "balancers" serve to support the larva before the legs develop. Their development has been shown to be induced by the underlying tissue. If epidermis is transplanted from a species that normally has balancers to one that does not, balancers will form. Apparently the inducer is present even in a species that has no balancers. But if the reciprocal transplant is made from a species without balancers to one that normally has them, there will be no balancers. Both species have the inducing agents, but in only one of them can the epidermis react by forming balancers.

All evidence indicates that the nuclei act directly only on cells in which they are found. They affect the differentiation of these cells, causing them to have one or another reaction to inducing agents, to develop in particular ways, to produce specific inducers, to make hormones. Through the various forms of interaction between cells, they have widespread effects on the body.

It was stated earlier that all nuclei seem to be identical and interchangeable. We are left, then, with a tremendous problem. How can identical nuclei participate in the differentiation of one cell into nerve and another into muscle? The question is still wide open, although recent work is beginning to shed some light. The work of the nucleus is done mainly by the *chromosomes*. Studying chromosome structure in an intact nucleus is something like studying the structure of a ball of wool without taking it apart. It is an extremely difficult job, but it is being done.

It has been found, for example, that the number of chromosomes, which has long been thought to be constant for all cells of a species, may actually vary from one tissue to another, provided that the tissues are *fully mature* and differentiated. Such cells rarely or never divide, which is one reason why this phenomenon has not been noticed earlier. It is easy to count chromosomes in dividing nuclei. Furthermore, suspicious swellings have been found on chromosomes of mature cells, the location of the swelling being characteristic of the kind of tissue. It is beginning to seem that different parts of the chromosomes are active in different cells. Possibly certain chromosomes degenerate and others duplicate themselves as the tissue differentiates. We will have to modify our previous conception of the interchangeability of nuclei and limit it to *embryonic* nuclei.

MALE AND FEMALE

"Boy or girl?" This is inevitably the first question asked about any baby. The only one who does not care is the baby himself, for he does not yet know how important the answer to this question is. In human life, the question of *what* sex is paramount in all social relationships.

Occasionally a baby is born with its sexual organs poorly developed and is raised as a girl even though it possesses a pair of undescended testes in its abdomen. Biologically, the child is male; physically, it is somewhere in between. But society makes no allowance for in-betweens. There are only two places where you can put the check after the word "sex" on an application blank, and only one check per person is allowed. When an in-between baby is born, a decision as to its sex must be made immediately so that the family can determine how to bring it up. When sex organs are badly formed, an error may be made which can persist for years. Sometimes the mistake is not found until the changes of adolescence make the tragic error unmistakable.

Until recently, doctors faced with this situation usually attempted to determine the biological sex of the patient, and treated him or her with hormones and surgery to produce superficial normality. But the social and psychological consequences of an apparent change of sex are devastating. Since there will probably never be any complete sexual and reproductive functioning anyway, doctors now do their best to give the patient the attributes of his socially determined sex, which is likely to be a much less troublesome solution to the problem.

Because of our experience in human society, we expect to find that the sharp differentiation of the sexes is a general law of nature. As we have seen, however, many animals and plants are male and female at the same time. Hermaphrodites possessing both kinds of sex organs are found in nearly all major groups of animals. Earthworms, pond snails, polyps, sponges, sea walnuts, flatworms, leeches, and barnacles are among the creatures that reproduce simultaneously as males and females, either by self-fertilization or by mutual fertilization of two individuals. In most cases, the testes occupy one clearly established position in the body and the ovaries are found somewhere else. Whether the sex gland develops into an ovary or a testis depends on its position, just as the development of any organ is controlled by its neighboring tissues.

There are also cases in which the kind of germ cell produced by an individual depends on the physiological state of the animal. Some tiny shrimp-like creatures parasitic on fishes are always male when young. If they make contact with a female, they move into her uterus and pass their lives as tiny parasites of parasites, living in the female and fertilizing her eggs. If they fail to find a female, they grow much larger and themselves become female. Whether their sex glands remain testes or turn into ovaries clearly depends on the circumstances in which the animal finds itself. There are other creatures, certain snails, for example, in which each individual changes sex as it grows older. Some oysters change sex every few days, the same sex gland producing eggs and sperms alternately.

Among the vertebrates, sex is usually more clearly delineated, though even here every individual starts life as a hermaphrodite. The vertebrate sex gland starts as a ridge in the mesoderm of the abdomen early in the life of the embryo, about the first week in humans. It seems to form as a result of induction by specialized cells—the primordial germ cells—that migrate in from a different part of the body. The ridge becomes organized into a more or less egg-shaped body containing an inner mass of tissue and a thick surrounding layer (Figure 8-3). About the fourth or fifth week in human embryonic life, the vital decision is made. Either the inner part of the organ will grow into a testis while the outer layer degenerates, or the outer layer will become the largest part of the ovary while the central material remains undeveloped. The primordial germ cells will become either eggs or sperms, depending on the course of development of the rest of the organ.

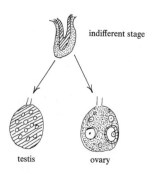

FIGURE 8-3. Differentiation of the sex gland.

The secondary sex organs of both sexes are found in the embryo. The four-week-old potential baby already has external sex organs, although it is impossible at this stage to tell whether the embryo is male or female. For example, it has a tiny tubercle in the groin which can either grow to become the largest part of the penis or remain small to form the clitoris, a small tubercle at the upper end of the female genitalia. A four-week-old human embryo is as hermaphroditic as an earthworm, although none of the organs are functional.

The early embryo grows along the crest of a ridge that separates the valleys of maleness and femaleness. At first the ridge is broad and the embryo easily stays halfway between the valleys. But as development proceeds, the ridge becomes narrower, until in the fourth week it is a knife-edge. The embryo must then fall rapidly down one slope or the other. A small push will start it inexorably down the hillside toward maleness or toward femaleness, and it can never again regain its ambiguous position on the crest of the ridge. What supplies the push?

Although the nature of this push is completely unknown, we do know its origin. Human sperms are of two kinds, male-determining and female-determining. When an egg is fertilized, the future sex of the child depends on what kind of sperm happens to unite with the egg. Since cell division produces duplicate nuclei, the primordial sex organ has in its nuclei a memory of the kind of sperm that fertilized the egg and responds accordingly. Somehow the nuclei determine whether the inner tissue grows into a testis or the outer tissue becomes an ovary. The primordial germ cells then grow into either sperms or eggs.

Becoming male or female involves much more than conversion of an indifferent sex gland into testis or ovary. By the time a baby is born, it already possesses all the reproductive and secondary sex organs characteristic of its sex, although they are almost in rudimentary form until the vital juices of adolescence convert the child into a man or woman. Perhaps these same juices, secreted long before the baby is born, bring the sex organs from the original, ambiguous form into the half-developed, differentiated state that allows the doctor to tell a new mother whether she has produced a boy or a girl.

Nipples are rudimentary until estrogen converts them into a usable part of a milk-production system. Testosterone can produce growth of the clitoris even in a full-grown woman. Is it this hormone, secreted by the newly formed testis, that converts the genital tubercle into a penis? This is a very attractive hypothesis, for it accounts neatly for the fact that once the four-week-old hermaphrodite has fallen off its ridge and formed a testis or ovary, the rest of the body follows until normal sex differentiation has occurred.

There is some evidence for this theory. The classic case occurs spontaneously. If a cow carries twin calves of opposite sex, and if the two placentas happen to grow together so that the blood of each flows through the vessels of both, the male calf will be normal, but the female becomes an inter-sex. Her external genitals and mammary glands may be normal, but she has testes and male sex ducts in her abdomen instead of ovaries. This can only be due to something that flows in the blood out of the body of her twin, and the material most likely to produce this result is some male hormone.

In amphibians, a similar situation, produced artificially, can cause complete sex reversal. In one experiment, newt embryos were surgically joined in pairs. Statistically, half of these pairs should be mixed sexes, but of ninety pairs grown, no mixed pairs were found. Most of the pairs were both male, although some were both female. Clearly, when the pairs were mixed, the male member of each pair was determining the sex of both.

It is the sex hormones that accomplish the sex reversal; experiments with salamanders have shown that the hormones alone can produce complete sex reversal. This cannot be the whole story, as the sex reversal is often incomplete. Surgical Siamese-twin wood frogs of opposite sex grow into a normal male and an intersexual female, like the cattle twins. The female hormone also can produce partial sex reversal; male rat embryos become intersexual in varying degrees if the mother is given large doses of estrogen in early pregnancy.

There is a breed of pigs in the New Hebrides Islands that is famous for its tendency toward intersexuality. Many of them are born with one ovary and one ovotestis. A normal ovary always contains some testis tissue which produces small amounts of testosterone, the remnant of the inner tissue of the primordial sex gland. But in these pigs, there is an unusual amount of this tissue. The animals are basically female, but the clitoris is abnormally large—a sure sign of an excess of male hormone. They pass through periods of heat, just as any female pig does, but they mate like males, courting and mounting other females. Undoubtedly the unusual balance of sex hormones has left these pigs stranded high on the ridge that divides the two sexes.

Even in adults, sex reversal is sometimes possible. Female birds normally have only a left ovary, the right sex gland remaining in an indifferent condition throughout life. If the ovary of a hen is removed, the right sex gland may develop into a testis, and the male hormone which it produces can change the bird into a rooster. There have been cases in which a hen, the devoted mother of many broods, has been converted into a fully functional rooster, complete with comb, wattles, crowing, treading, aggressiveness, and male mating behavior. On occasion such "hens" have even become fathers.

The rare cases of human intersexuality are usually boys with undeveloped sex organs. The penis is so small as to be mistaken for a clitoris. The two halves of the scrotum, instead of growing together from the sides and joining down the middle to form a sac, remain separate to form a structure resembling the female vulva. The testes remain undescended in their original position in the abdomen. Since both descent of the testes and growth of the penis are known to be produced by testosterone, it is likely that the abnormality is the result of a deficiency of this hormone.

All the evidence, then, indicates that the hormones play an important part in the determination of sex. However, it is probably not the whole story, for complete sex reversal of the embryo by hormone treatment has been accomplished in only a few species of amphibians; generally, intersexes are produced. There is still a great deal to be learned about the interactions of the two sex hormones with each other and with the embryo in which they are formed.

9

‧‧‧‧‧‧‧‧‧‧‧‧‧‧‧‧‧‧‧‧‧‧‧‧‧‧‧‧‧‧‧‧‧‧‧‧‧

Reproduction
at the Cell Level

A hundred and fifty years ago, biologists still disagreed on the fundamental question of whether the life of a plant resides in the thick, easily seen walls of the tiny boxes that they found in plant tissues, or in the tiny blob of colorless jelly within the box. When it was shown that animal cells possessed the blob of jelly but not the thick wall, and that the walls remained practically unchanged long after the death of a plant cell, it became clear that the tiny droplets within are actually the fundamental units of life. There seemed to be little difference between the living cells of various animals and plants, and the living jelly was named *protoplasm*.

With the earliest microscopes it was a distinct accomplishment to see the cells. Techniques have improved so much since then that we are now able to study minute details of cell structure. We know that these living globules have a rich and varied internal structure, a variety of parts

174 « «

that could not have been dreamed of when the early studies of cells were being done. The first clue to the fact that a cell is not simply a formless blob of jelly was the discovery of the *nucleus,* a tiny sphere of denser material usually found near the center of the cell. Almost as soon as the nucleus was discovered, it was realized that this globule is chemically different from the rest of the cell, which is now known as the *cytoplasm.* In fact, it was this chemical difference that made the nucleus visible, for it was discovered by virtue of the fact that it reacts differently with certain dyes, and is therefore easily seen against a differently colored cytoplasm when appropriate staining techniques are used. This discovery has stimulated others, and many unusual, even bizarre, arrangements of living material have since been found. For a while there was some dispute about the fundamental nature of the cell, but the most recent work seems to bear out the old idea that the smallest functional unit of life consists of a nucleus surrounded by a mass of cytoplasm.

STRUCTURE OF CELLS

With further improvements in optics and in techniques of study, still smaller structures have been found in both the nucleus and the cytoplasm. The nucleus is composed of a membranous sac enclosing a thin gel in which nucleoli (small bodies found in the nuclei of most cells) and chromosomes reside. In the cytoplasm, the microscope reveals mitochondria, Golgi apparatus, globules, and vacuoles. All nuclei are remarkably similar, but cytoplasm of different organisms, or of different parts of the same organism, always has special structures associated with the particular function of the cell. Thus there is an endless variety of plastids, centrosomes, vacuoles, fibers, cilia, and so on, giving each type of cell a characteristic structure.

It was in the late 1930's that a great technological breakthrough made still finer details of structure visible to us. With the electron microscope, we can now see a complex and exquisitely detailed structure within the various threads and granules, droplets and fibers of the cell. A mitochondrion, properly stained and placed under an ordinary microscope, looks like a tiny rod. You can enlarge it as much as you wish by using a more powerful eyepiece or by photographic enlargement, and it then looks like a large, blurry rod. But if it is illuminated with a beam of electrons instead of with light, and if the beam is focused with electromagnets instead of lenses, a new world of detail emerges. The mitochondrion is now seen to consist of a hollow, double-walled box containing a large number of double shelves projecting inward from the walls.

The electron microscope is even capable of revealing individually some of the giant-sized molecules of cells. The study of cell chemistry is also advancing rapidly, and occasionally it can help us to deduce the location of individual molecules. Exciting things are happening in this field of science, where the chemical study of ever larger molecules is merging with the biological study of ever-smaller cell structures.

Figure 9-1 shows a composite picture of a cell. It is safe to call the nucleus typical, but cytoplasms vary so much that no single cell can be called typical. The diagram includes all the structures that are found in most animal cells, shown in their usual relationships to each other. Special structures that are found only in specialized cells are omitted.

The nucleus is partially isolated from the rest of the cell by a rather tough, elastic, *nuclear membrane*. This membrane consists of a double layer of insoluble proteins and fats, penetrated at intervals by holes so small as to be invisible even under the electron microscope. Nucleus and cytoplasm

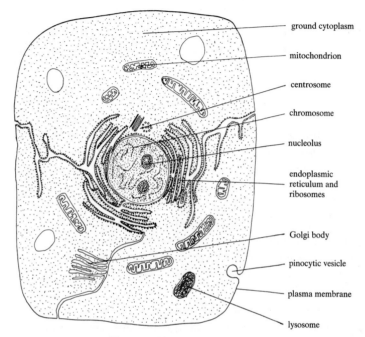

ground cytoplasm

mitochondrion

centrosome

chromosome

nucleolus

endoplasmic
reticulum and
ribosomes

Golgi body

pinocytic vesicle

plasma membrane

lysosome

FIGURE 9-1. A typical cell.

are separate entities, but interact with each other by exchanging materials through these holes. Within the nucleus,
the tangled, thread-like *chromosomes* and a couple of glob-
ular *nucleoli* lie embedded in the *nuclear sap*.

As we saw in Chapter 8, the nucleus has an enormous
influence on every stage of the development process. It is
now firmly established that the chromosomes carry, in the
form of a chemical code, instructions for development. These
instructions are passed to the cytoplasm by chemical means.
The discovery of the details of this process is the great biochemical triumph of the 1950's; breaking the code is the
task of the 1960's. We will take a much closer look at this
process in Chapters 10 and 11.

The entire cytoplasm is surrounded by a *plasma membrane,* a thin sheet of protein and fat molecules. In many cells such as the protozoa, there are additional coats outside this membrane, as the membrane is too weak to hold the cell together. The typical external coat of a plant cell is thick, rigid, and nonliving, and is called the *cell wall.* The cytoplasm itself appears structureless under an ordinary microscope, but with an electron microscope it is possible to see a complex network of membranes, concentrated near the nucleus. This *endoplasmic reticulum* serves as the boundary for some kind of canal system. According to one theory, these canals are a pathway for circulation of fluids in the cell and interchange of materials between nucleus and cytoplasm. Embedded in the membranes are large numbers of tiny specks called *ribosomes,* where new proteins are made. The canals run through a rather uniform protein-water gel called the *ground cytoplasm.*

Several kinds of special structures are found in the cytoplasm. Near one side of the nucleus (in animal cells and primitive algae only) is a pair of *centrioles,* each of which consists of a bundle of eleven short, tubular fibers, nine arranged in a ring surrounding the other two. The bundles are oriented perpendicular to each other and are important in division of the cell and in the growth of the living, hairlike processes found in many cells, called *cilia* and *flagella.* Concentrated near the nucleus is a large number of short, rodlike *mitochondria,* which have been called the engine of the cell. It is here that the cell's food is oxidized and its energy is transferred to a special chemical that can carry it to the rest of the cell. The hollow, flattened sacs of the Golgi apparatus are still a mystery. They are connected to channels of the endoplasmic reticulum and are thought to serve either as membrane-factories or producers of cell secretions.

Lysosomes are now known to be different in structure from the mitochondria, though the two were long confused. If a lysosome is punctured, its contents spill into the cytoplasm and destroy the cell by digestion in a short time. These bodies apparently have the function of digestion of the cell's food materials. The *pinocytic vesicles,* discovered recently, are tiny globules formed by ingrowth and pinching off of the cell membrane. They apparently ingest water, and perhaps dissolved materials and tiny granules as well.

In addition to these structures, which are found in most cells, there is a variety of special structures doing particular jobs in specialized cells. Many plant cells have *plastids,* usually tiny globules containing pigment. In green leaves and stems, the pigment is chlorophyll, which provides the chemical energy of the cell by conversion of sunlight. Other pigments in plastids give color to flowers. Hairlike cilia cover the surface of a *Paramecium* and propel it through the water. Cilia are also found in the human trachea, where they move dust up into the throat and keep it out of the lungs, and in the fallopian tubes, where they move eggs down into the uterus. Muscle cells have their fibrils, nerve cells their axons and Nissl bodies, gland cells their secretory granules, and so on for every specialized cell.

CELL REPRODUCTION

There are few rules general enough to apply to all living creatures. One famous dictum, now one hundred and fifty years old, sounds like those broad, sweeping generalizations that natural philosophers of those days found so appealing. It states *"omne cellula e cellule,"* or "every cell comes from a cell." If we are willing to accept a somewhat broader concept of a cell than was usual in those days, the dictum can still be accepted today. This is remarkable vigor for such a broad biological generalization.

Most one-celled organisms—bacteria, protozoa, and the simpler algae and fungi—commonly reproduce by splitting in half. Typically in protozoa, as in most animal cells, the outermost layer of cytoplasm is denser and more elastic than the central part of the cell where the nucleus is located. It is this outer layer that seems to perform the mechanical part of the cell-splitting process. An indentation appears in its surface in the form of a ring completely encircling the cell. The indentation gets deeper until it meets itself in the center, dividing the cell into two parts.

Plant cells generally split by a different process: tiny vesicles appear near the middle of the cell, arranged in a sheet across the cell. They then coalesce to divide the cell and serve as a base around which the cell cytoplasm deposits cellulose to form the cell wall that is so characteristic of plant cells. In both cases, the division of the cell into two is preceded by a division of the nucleus, so that each of the daughter cells has its own nucleus.

There seems to be an upper limit to the size of a cell. Probably the control that the nucleus exerts over the chemical processes in the cytoplasm of most cells cannot extend very far from the nucleus, so a cell must divide when it grows beyond a certain size. There is no limit to the growing ability of an amoeba. It can regenerate without limit any pieces that are removed, but it will not divide unless it is allowed to reach a certain size.

There are a number of variations on this simple method of asexual reproduction among simpler organisms. Some protozoa divide into a large number of cells instead of two. In these cases, the nucleus divides repeatedly to form a large cell with many nuclei, and the cell then divides into many small ones, each with its nucleus. In other species, most of the life of the animal is passed in the many-nuclei form, and the creature divides at intervals into smaller masses with only a few nuclei each. It is in these "social amebae" that our concept of the cell requires some stretching, but it seems to be true that each nucleus controls the activity of a small mass of cytoplasm surrounding it. This semi-isolated body of cytoplasm with its nucleus acts functionally as a cell, even though it is not separated from its neighbors by a membrane.

Many protozoa and algae divide repeatedly without separation of cells, so that colonies of cells are formed. *Oedogonium,* which we looked at in Chapter 3, is a colonial organism of this type. The similarity of this process with the development of a zygote into a many-celled organism is striking, the only difference being that in the latter case, the cells differentiate. A cleaving zygote is much like a colony of undifferentiated cells, for, as we have seen, it can be divided in various ways without disturbing the course of its development. All cell division, whether of an *Ameba* to form two individuals or of a cell of your skin to replace one that has fallen off, has many marked similarities.

Cell division is not as simple as it looks. As Figure 9-1 shows, the cell has an extraordinarily complex structure, which must be retained or regenerated through cell division. Some of the structures are formed as needed, but others are of a more or less permanent nature. The plasma membrane is no problem; it quickly reforms from cytoplasmic material if it is injured in any way, so that there is always enough for however many daughter cells may be formed. The pinocytic vesicles are temporary structures, formed as needed and disappearing when they are no longer of any value.

Other parts of the cell are of a more permanent nature. The nuclear membrane and the nucleoli are always found within the nucleus, but they disappear when the cell starts to divide and form anew in each daughter cell after division of the cell is complete. Golgi apparatus also behaves in this way, but there is some evidence that the new apparatus forms out of fragments of the old. Specialized structures such as cilia must be formed anew in the daughter cells. Both cilia and flagella seem to form only as a result of the activity of centrioles.

The centrioles of the cell require some special attention, since they are important in the division of animal cells. As far as we know, centrioles are strictly self-reproducing structures; that is, new centrioles form only by the division of existing ones. The electron microscope has shown that a nondividing animal cell has two centrioles oriented at right angles to each other. When the cell is about to divide, they separate from each other and a new, daughter centriole sprouts from each member of the pair. Thus each daughter cell has a mature pair of centrioles as soon as it is formed. In cells that form cilia or flagella, additional centriole division may occur, the extra centrioles forming the *basal granules* at the root of each cilium. All cilia and flagella are built, like centrioles, out of a ring of nine tubular filaments surrounding a central pair.

There are other self-reproducing elements within cells. When the ingrowing membrane divides a cell into two daughters, the mitochondria are apportioned between the two daughters at random. There is need for proof, but present evidence indicates that as the cell grows, the mitochondria reproduce themselves to restore the number that a mature cell needs. We are sure that this is the way new plastids are supplied, and there is reason to believe that mitochondria and plastids are related.

MITOSIS

The self-reproduction of chromosomes is a more complex problem, for the information that they carry must also be duplicated. There seem to be many thousands of separate pieces of information, or *genes,* in each chromosome, an achievement in microminiaturization that a computer designer might well envy. So far as we know, division of a cell must always be preceded by duplication of every chromosome, with every gene making an exact copy of itself at the correct location in the new chromosome.

It may be difficult to see how myriads of cells containing identical information could differentiate into the various cells in the body. Then imagine an English teacher assigning a class a report on a novel. Each student reads the same novel, but the author's words fall on a variety of minds. Each student sees something different in the book, reacts to a different part, or interprets what he has read according to his own mental set. In the same way, different parts of the chromosomal instructions are used, and in different ways, by different cytoplasms. Inducing agents from neighboring tissues, chemical stimuli from the environment, and existing differentiation will all determine which part of the message contained in the nucleus will be used by the cytoplasm. Having read it, the cytoplasm in its response will react back on the chromosomes.

There are great differences between a fully differentiated cell and an embryonic cell. In an adult organism, most cells have grown special structures to enable them to perform their functions, and in doing so have sacrificed their ability to divide. But certain cells in the connective and epithelial tissues remain unspecialized and capable of division as long as the animal lives. The difference between these two kinds of cells can be detected within a few hours after the cell division which formed them.

Embryonic nuclei of any given species have a characteristic number of chromosomes; each human nucleus, for example, ordinarily contains forty-six chromosomes. If the cell is to divide again, each of these chromosomes soon doubles its thickness and splits lengthwise, becoming a

Siamese-twin pair. When, at a later time, the cell divides, all forty-six pairs of Siamese twins are separated, one member of each pair going into each of the two daughter cells. Thus, each daughter cell is born with a full set of forty-six chromosomes, identical to those of the parent. Within an hour or two, each daughter cell again begins either to duplicate its chromosomes in preparation for the next division or to form special structures and settle down into a working life. In some adult tissues, such as the skin, the intestinal lining, and the testis tubules, cell division is constantly occurring. Every time a cell divides one of the daughter cells prepares for division while the other changes into a functioning, nondividing cell.

The apportionment of chromosomes between daughter cells at the time of cell division is called *mitosis,* and is a remarkable process. It involves nearly every part of the cell in a clearly ordered sequence of events that follow each other in approximately the same way in all cells. Preparation for mitosis involves a series of invisible events that may take anywhere from a half-hour to many days. The chromosomes must duplicate themselves to form identical pairs. The centrioles (in animal cells) separate, and each one produces its perpendicular offspring to turn itself into a pair. The special proteins needed for the actual mitosis are manufactured in the cytoplasm. When all is ready, each part of the cell goes through its particular motions like a well-rehearsed ballet troupe, leading to the dramatic climax in which the cell divides in two.

The start of mitosis (see Figure 9-2) is marked by the separation of the centrioles, which move to opposite ends of the cell. Their new positions mark the two poles around which the new cells will be organized. As the centrioles move apart, they become centers for the radial growth of fibers formed in the adjacent cytoplasm. These fibers grow

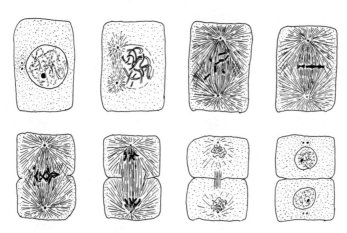

FIGURE 9-2. Mitosis in an animal cell.

outward until they may fill nearly the whole cell. One special group of fibers, connecting from one centriole to the other, form the *mitotic spindle*. The nucleus also has been reorganizing; the nuclear membrane and nucleoli have disappeared, destroying the sharp distinction between nucleus and cytoplasm. The chromosomes, each already split down the middle, coil up into a helix, the shape of a spring. Since the helix is tightly coiled, the chromosomes now look like short, fat rods instead of long fibers. There is a special point on chromosomes by which each becomes attached to a spindle fiber. The fibers now contract, pulling the chromosomes into position halfway between the centrioles.

Now comes the division. We have each chromosome in the middle of the cell. From each half of any chromosome, a spindle fiber runs from the spindle-attachment point to one of the centrioles, so that each half of the chromosome is connected to a different pole of the cell. The spindle fibers continue to shorten, pulling the chromosomes in half. Half of each chromosome is pulled toward each pole of the cell.

When the half-chromosomes are well separated, the cell divides in half in such a way that one half of each chromosome is now in each daughter cell. Then the mitotic spindle degenerates and the chromosomes uncoil and tangle around each other, while a new nuclear membrane forms around the tangle in each daughter cell. Two or more of the chromosomes contain special points that generate new nucleoli. A single cell has become two, each with a full set of chromosomes, identical with the set in the original parent cell.

The details of mitosis vary considerably. Plants have no visible centrioles, but form a spindle anyway. If you have a philosophical turn of mind, you may have been wondering whether there is any great, unifying principle underlying all the reproductive processes you have been reading about. Mitosis certainly is a part of any such unification. All reproduction implies cell reproduction, and cell reproduction involves the exact duplication of nuclei. In spite of variations that do exist, the mitosis process, the exact duplication of the code in the chromosomes in each cell generation, occurs whenever cells divide. As you read further, you will find a still more profound generalization underlying the mitosis seen through a microscope.

DIPLOID AND HAPLOID

As we saw earlier in the chapter, whenever sexual reproduction takes place, a readjustment of chromosome number is necessary. If human sex cells contained forty-six chromosomes each, the zygote would have ninety-two. Clearly, there must be some mechanism by which the correct chromosome number is restored. As we have noted, the problem is easily solved by reduction division, which reduces the chromosome number to half. In animals, this takes place when gametes are formed, while in plants it occurs in the production of spores.

The twenty-three chromosomes in a human sperm or egg are all different and constitute a set. The members of the set are distinguishable, and have been assigned numbers from one to twenty-three, so that a cytologist can intelligently refer to any given chromosome if he wants to. The egg also contains a full set of twenty-three chromosomes, identical in appearance to the set in the sperm (with one exception, noted below). The forty-six chromosomes of a body cell, therefore, are actually twenty-three pairs, for each cell contains two of each kind. After fertilization, it is not possible to tell whether a given chromosome was donated by the egg or the sperm, but it is possible to tell which kind of chromosome is being studied in terms of its number in the set. In fully mature, differentiated cells, not all parts of the chromosome set are needed, and there is now a good deal of evidence that some chromosomes, or parts of chromosomes, may disappear while others make extra copies of themselves. Cells in which this has happened apparently never divide again.

Human sperms are made in the walls of a couple of dozen coiled tubules in the testes. The tubule walls consist of cells with the usual forty-six chromosomes each. These cells are constantly dividing by mitosis, forming an endless supply of forty-six-chromosome cells from which sperms are made. The new cells are forced toward the center of the tubule by the division of cells behind them, and when they are halfway to the center, they undergo a different kind of division—reduction division. This converts each forty-six-chromosome cell into four twenty-three-chromosome cells, each of which becomes a sperm.

Egg cells must also reduce their chromosome number

to half. The "egg" has a full forty-six chromosomes when it is released from the ovary, and it then divides twice to form four cells with twenty-three chromosomes each, just as in the production of sperms. In this case, however, the cytoplasm does not divide equally, so that nearly all of the cytoplasm ends up in one of the four haploid cells. This one becomes the egg and is the only one of the cells that has any further use. In fact, the second division usually does not occur in the first of the tiny cells, the one that carries off half the chromosome material.

An analogy might help us understand how this reduction of chromosome number occurs. Suppose each year the League of Dancing Twins holds a national convention, that duplicates the events that occur when chromosomes are apportioned among different sperms. Each of the twenty-three cities that have chapters of this organization selects two pairs of twins to attend the convention, one pair of boys and one pair of girls. For this discussion, we will separate them, rather than consider them to be of the Siamese variety. At the grand ball that winds up the festivities, all forty-six pairs of twins are on the floor, wandering around and talking to each other, but always keeping in pairs, as twins sometimes tend to do. When the music starts, they keep wandering around until each finds the other pair from their own home town. Then the four representatives of each town dance together in a group called a *tetrad*. Each tetrad remains intact, the four representatives of each town remaining together until the ballet master calls out "first division." At this signal, each tetrad splits in half, two members moving to the north wall of the ballroom and the other two to the south.

The new pairs may be of the same or of opposite sexes, depending on which way they happen to be facing when the music stops. When all the pairs have reached the north and south walls, the ballet master calls "second division," and the pairs now split again, one member of each pair moving eastward and the other westward. The result is that each corner of the room contains twenty-three people. These will be variously assorted as to sex, but there will be exactly one representative of each town in each corner. Each group of twenty-three is then taken to a bus and—but you can finish the story yourself if you like.

This is the choreography that results in the reduction of chromosome number when sperms form. The forty-six chromosomes, each previously split into a pair, squirm around until each chromosome has lined up alongside its opposite number from the other set, forming a tetrad (Figure 9-3). Then they begin to coil and shorten, as for ordinary mitosis, but forming twenty-three short, fat tetrads rather than forty-six short, fat chromosomes. The tetrads line up at the center of the spindle and are pulled in half. The cell now divides and the spindle degenerates, but instead of each cell forming a new nucleus, each immediately forms a new spindle. The half-tetrads line up again and are pulled in half once more, so that four cells are formed, each containing one-fourth of each tetrad. The result is that each of the four cells has one full set of twenty-three chromosomes. Each cell organizes the twenty-three chromosomes into a nucleus, and the cell proceeds to turn into a sperm.

One important point has been omitted. While the chromosomes were in the tetrad stage, they interchanged pieces. It is as though our dancers indiscriminately traded arms and legs while the group of four was dancing together, but each of the four members always emerged with a full quota of parts. Each of the twenty-three chromosomes of the sperm consists of parts of each of the two corresponding chromosomes in the original cell. Traced back to the preceding generation, each chromosome in a man's sperm is

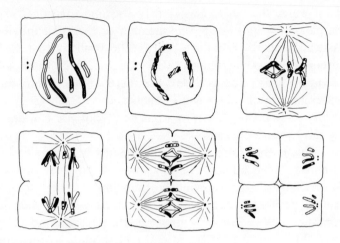

FIGURE 9-3. Reduction division.

made of pieces originally obtained from his mother and other pieces originally from his father. The same, of course, may be said of the chromosomes of the egg.

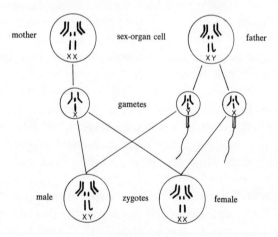

FIGURE 9-4. Sex determination in the fruit fly.

DETERMINATION OF SEX

We discussed the determination of sex in Chapter 8, stating that a man produces two kinds of sperms, one male-determining and the other female-determining. We are now in a position to examine this process in more detail. The mechanism of sex determination was first discovered in studies of that eminently useful little pest, the fruit fly. Four chromosomes make up a full set in this animal (Figure 9-4), and in the female, four perfectly matched pairs of chromosomes are found per cell. In the male, however, there are only three matched pairs, identical with three of the pairs in the female. The other pair in the male consists of one member (the *X-chromosome*) which looks just like the first pair of chromosomes of the female, and a second chromosome that is not found in females at all. This is the *Y-chromosome,* which is longer than the X and refuses to take the ordinary chromosome stains except in a small region.

In the ovaries of the female, a pair of X-chromosomes forms a tetrad, and every egg contains an X. In the testes of the male, a tetrad is formed by an X and a Y. Of the four sperms formed at reduction division, then, two contain the X-chromosome and the other two have a Y. When an X-bearing sperm fertilizes an egg, the zygote has two X-chromosomes (XX) and becomes a female. When a Y-bearing sperm fertilizes an egg, the zygote is XY and becomes a male.

The same chromosomal mechanism of sex determination has been found in a great many other animals, including man, although there are some variations. In birds, butterflies, frogs, and probably some other groups, all sperms are alike, and there are two kinds of eggs. The males are said to be WW and the females ZW. In many insects, there is no Y-chromosome at all, so the female is XX as usual, but the male is XO. Then it is the absence of an X-chromosome in the sperm that is the determining factor in producing a male. In bees, the males grow from unfertilized eggs, and every cell of the adult is haploid. They form sperms by ordinary mitosis. If an egg is fertilized, it grows into a female; if not, into a male. In many of the lower animals, as we saw in Chapter 3, sex is not as sharply delineated as we expect it to be, and may change quite easily. It probably has nothing to do with chromosomes in these cases.

Does a Y-chromosome make a fruit fly male? Soon after the mechanism of sex determination was found, this question was vigorously attacked by means of abnormal flies. Under some conditions, it is possible to produce fruit flies with an unusual number of chromosomes. It was then found that the Y-chromosome really had little or nothing to do with sex determination! An XYY fly (one X, two Y's) or an XO fly (one X, no Y's) is physically male if it has the usual numbers of other chromosomes. These flies are usually sterile, but their body structure is normal. On the other hand, XXY or XXYY flies are female. The fact that XXX flies are "superfemale," that is, female with their feminine features exaggerated, indicates that the X chromosomes produces femaleness. Supermale flies result if the sex chromosomes are XY or XO and there are *three* each of the other chromosomes rather than the usual two. It is apparently the other chromosomes, not the X and Y at all, that produce maleness. The actual sex depends on the ratio between the number of X-chromosomes and the number of nonsex chromosomes. The Y-chromosomes have little or nothing to do with it.

Abnormal mitoses during development of the fly can produce individuals that are female on the left side of the body and male on the right, or even mixed-up patches of male and female throughout. Some interesting experiments are now being done on the behavior of fruit flies with male sex organs and female brains, and vice versa. In vertebrates, this kind of sexual patchwork is not easily attainable because the sexuality of the individual is so strongly influenced by hormones. Nevertheless, there is now evidence that every normal woman is a genetic patchwork. Most body cells of women do not contain two X-chromosomes, only one, the other having been converted into a formless mass. Cases have been found in which the two X-chromosomes are different, producing two distinguishable kinds of chemical behavior in the cells. Tests have shown that in these cases one kind of X-chromosome is found in some cells, and the other kind is found in the rest. The body consists of patches of cells with the same kind of X-chromosome. The indication is that about the third week of embryonic life one X-chromosome in every cell degenerates, with no regularity determining which one is lost in any given cell. As the body grows, each cell gives rise to a patch of tissue, every cell of which has the same X-chromosome.

There is an intersexual condition called Klinefelter's syndrome, which doctors see occasionally. The patient is an unusually tall, thin man with tiny, nonfunctional testes and well-developed breasts. It is similar to some other intersexual conditions and was long thought to be due to some hormonal abnormality. But it is now possible to study human chromosomes in great detail.

If, for example, white blood cells are treated to make them divide, which they do not ordinarily do, and colchicine is added, the cell division stops at the stage at which the chromosomes are short and fat, lined up on the spindle. In this state, they can easily be seen and studied separately. If a salt solution of low concentration is added, the cells take in water, swell, and burst, separating the chromosomes for convenient study. With this technique, it has been found that victims of Klinefelter's syndrome are *genetic* intersexes, since their sex chromosomes are XXY!

A number of different kinds of abnormalities due to the wrong number of sex chromosomes have been found. They occur when abnormal reduction division puts the wrong number of sex chromosomes into a gamete. For example, if both the X- and the Y-chromosomes got into a single sperm and if this sperm were to fertilize an egg, the zygote would be XXY and would grow into a Klinefelter male. If there were no X or Y in the sperm, the zygote would have only a single X-chromosome and would grow into a woman with tiny ovaries and all sexual characteristics undeveloped—a sufferer from Turner's syndrome. These and other cases make it clear that the X- and Y-chromosomes function quite differently in human beings than they do in fruit flies. The human Y *does* produce maleness, for the Klinefelter XXY's are male, not female as in the fruit fly. On the other hand, a single X-chromosome is not sufficient to produce all the female characteristics.

This interesting problem is just beginning to be explored. We would like to know how the sex chromosomes act in many species. We would like to know how the sex chromosomes go about sending the embryo down one side of the sex-determination ridge or the other, and particularly to what extent hormones are involved in the process. The sex-determination mechanism should produce both sexes in equal numbers; we would like to know why one hundred and six boys are born for every one hundred girls. Every answer, as it should, breeds questions.

10

~~~~~~~~~~~~~~~~~~~~~~~~~~~~~~~

The Chemical Structure of Cells

Let us imagine a rather naïve chemist who sets out on the task of creating life, perhaps in response to a teacher's insistence that each student perform some kind of "science project." He gets a mouse and proceeds to perform a chemical analysis. After many hours of careful and tedious labor, he discovers that his sample consists very largely of four elements—carbon, oxygen, hydrogen, and nitrogen. With reasonable care, he could find small amounts of sulfur, magnesium, sodium, chlorine, phosphorus, calcium, potassium, iron, and a few others. If he is quite expert as well as naïve—a combination difficult to imagine, but necessary for this purpose—he would discover extremely minute amounts of boron, iodine, zinc, copper, silicon, and some thirty other elements. Having found out what his sample is made of, he then takes correct amounts of each element, mixes them, and heats gently, expecting the materials to combine to form a mouse.

Why does the experiment fail? If you can remember as far back as Chapter 1, you will realize that a nineteenth-century biologist might tell our chemist that he had no way of adding *élan vital,* the mysterious spirit of life. Since this concept has long since been abandoned, we must find some other way to explain why the correct combination of elements does not form a mouse. We need look no further than the fundamental rule of nature that the whole of anything is always more than the sum of its parts, Euclid to the contrary notwithstanding. A building is not just bricks, mortar, wood, and plaster; it consists of all these materials and many others, in the proper proportions, *organized* in a certain way. The creation of this organization is the work of the carpenters, masons, electricians, plumbers, architects, contractors and all the rest of the men who convert raw materials into a place to live. This rule applies to the mouse to an even greater degree than it does to a building, for the mouse has a much more complex organization.

LEVELS OF ORGANIZATION

If we were to undertake the job of making a mouse from its constituent elements, we would first have to combine the elements into compounds. Some of the hydrogen and oxygen, for example, would be combined to make water, which accounts for three-quarters of the weight of the mouse. Some of the sodium and chlorine might be used to make ordinary salt. We would need a lot of the sugar called glucose, which would be made of carbon, hydrogen, and oxygen. In all, several thousand chemical compounds would be needed, each in exactly the right amount. Most of them belong to the general category of organic compounds composed chiefly of carbon, oxygen, and hydrogen, with considerable amounts of nitrogen, sulfur, phosphorus, and so on.

By mixing all these compounds together, we would be

no more successful in making a mouse than after our first try at mixing the separate elements. The next step would have to be uniting these materials to form cells. To make a single cell, exact amounts of each of thousands of compounds would be needed. Furthermore, they would have to be combined molecule by molecule, with each molecule in its correct place to make the cell membranes, chromosomes, mitochondria, and the other formed structures within the cell. Then we would have to build the cell by putting each of these parts in correct relationship to the others. This would have to be done perhaps a trillion times and in a thousand different ways to make all the varied cells of the mouse's body.

We are far from finished. Now we must make organs by selecting the right kinds of cells and placing them in correct orientation to each other, adding appropriate amounts of noncellular material such as body fluids and fibers. Then we must combine the organs correctly, supplying blood vessels and nerves to ramify throughout the body and unite the organs into a functioning whole. Now would anyone like to try to make a mouse?

It is this fantastic complexity of structure that makes the synthesis of a mouse impossible. Living creatures can be created only because those that already live have the ability to duplicate their structure, to reproduce. Life is organized on a hierarchy of levels: atoms combine to make molecules, molecules to make cell organelles, organelles to make cells, and cells to make the tissues and organs that constitute a many-celled organism. Reproduction occurs at all levels. Many-celled creatures reproduce by various sexual and asexual methods, as we have seen. Work on regeneration has shown that many tissues can duplicate themselves to repair injuries to the body.

Both of these processes require that cells divide to form

additional tissue. Within the cells, mitochondria, centrioles, and chromosomes duplicate themselves to supply the materials needed for the division of a cell into two complete daughters. And recent biochemical research has revealed that in one crucial area at least, the very molecules are able to reproduce themselves. In fact, they *must* do so to prepare the way for the division of cells that is necessary for all reproduction at higher levels. The reproduction of molecules is therefore at the very heart of all biological reproduction.

Atoms do not reproduce themselves. Biological reproduction is a process of using available atoms to make copies of existing structures. Animals take in food which always consists of the highly organized material of animals and plants, and then break down the existing structure by digestion. Green plants get their raw materials from still simpler matter, water and minerals from the soil and carbon dioxide from the air. In either case, the raw materials are built step by step into the complex structure of the body. You are what you eat, in a quite literal sense, for the hamburger and ice cream that you ate yesterday is converted by your body into cells that are more or less duplicates of the cells that are already present. Carbon, the basic structural material of the molecules of life, passes from one living creature to another in an endless chain, entering into new combinations, but always keeping its identity.

About one part in four hundred of the air is carbon dioxide. This great reservoir of the chemical element most characteristic of living creatures is constantly being replenished by three processes: fires of organic matter, such as wood, coal, oil and gas; volcanoes, where the heat is great enough to break down such carbonate rocks as marble and limestone; and the excretion of living creatures, which pass out carbon dioxide as waste products of their life processes.

Green plants take in this carbon dioxide and endow it with the energy that all living things use by incorporating it into the molecule of sugar, obtaining the energy for the process by exposing their green leaves to the sun. The sugar can then be converted into starch, into fats and oils, and into many other energy-rich materials that make up the structure of any organism.

Either the plant, or the animal that eats the plant, or the animal that eats the animal that eats the plant, or the bacteria that feed on the body of the animal or the plant, may use these chemicals, may oxidize them to provide the energy they need. In doing so, they return the carbon to the air in the form of carbon dioxide.

In this entire cycle, the total amount of carbon has not changed. The other elements of life—nitrogen, oxygen, phosphorous, etc.—go through similar cycles, being recombined into different chemicals in whatever organism they find themselves, but always remaining constant in total amount. Reproduction is part of the building phase of these cycles, the reorganization of the atoms into new forms that duplicate the organization of the animal or plant in which the process occurs.

If we are to explore this chemical reproductive process more fully, we will have to know a little more about the nature of these chemicals of life.

ORGANIZATION AT THE CHEMICAL LEVEL

The first thing to realize is the scale of size involved when we start to discuss molecules. They are inconceivably small. If you had started when the earth began five billion years ago to put sugar molecules into a cup, one every second, you would by now have accumulated barely enough sugar to flavor a single drop of coffee. These molecules have never been seen, although recent developments in electron microscopy and the new field-emission microscope may soon make it possible to obtain some sort of image of them. And yet the chemist, in his daily work, speaks of the intimate details of the structure of the molecule with considerable assurance. It would take us far afield to investigate the methods by which the chemist deduces the structure of molecules, so I will have to ask you to take all that follows on faith.

Early chemists classified all materials as either *organic* or *inorganic*. Air, minerals, water, and other materials of nonliving origin were inorganic; the chemicals found in living things were organic; and the synthesis of organic chemicals was believed to be a function of the *élan vital* and therefore could never be accomplished in a test tube. The synthesis, in the laboratory, of some half a million organic chemicals during the last century has forced us to modify this position somewhat. We still retain the distinction between organic and inorganic chemicals, but the words have acquired new meanings. Many inorganic chemicals are found in living creatures, and organic materials are routinely made in laboratories. Most inorganic chemicals are composed not of molecules, but of electrically charged particles called *ions*. A crystal of salt consists of two kinds of ions: atoms of sodium bearing an excess positive charge, and atoms of chlorine bearing an excess negative charge. Some ions consist of more than one atom: sulfuric acid is composed of negative ions made of one atom of sulfur and four of oxygen ($SO_4 -$) and positive ions made of one atom of oxygen and three of hydrogen (H_3O+), all thoroughly mixed together with many molecules of water (H_2O). The ions are small and usually contain no carbon.

Organic chemicals are characterized by three properties: (1) they contain carbon, (2) they form very large combinations of atoms, and (3) the combinations are usually uncharged molecules rather than charged ions. Even in the earliest days of chemistry when the whole subject was suffused with vitalism, it was realized that carbon is unique among the atoms in its ability to produce the special properties of the molecules of organic chemicals. The bonding of atoms to form molecules was pictured, in those days, as due to some kind of "hook" that every atom possessed, enabling it to fasten to the hooks of other atoms. Carbon has four of these hooks which can fasten onto the hooks of atoms of oxygen or hydrogen or chlorine. Because of the four hooks, and for some other mysterious reasons, carbon atoms can connect to each other to form long chains, the basis for the large size, great complexity, and wide variability of organic chemicals.

The hook model has long since been replaced by better ones, but it will do for our purposes, for we have no need to investigate the nature of chemical bonding. Thus we may think of a water molecule as consisting of an oxygen atom, which always has two hooks fastened to the single hooks of each of two hydrogen atoms. This can be represented schematically as in the first formula in Figure 10-1. The O stands for an atom of oxygen, and the H's for hydrogen atoms. The lines represent pairs of interlocking hooks joining the atoms together. To the right is the formula for the gas methane, in which each of the four hooks of a carbon atom is connected to the single hook of a hydrogen. The carbon dioxide molecule is formed when oxygens join to the carbon by "double bonds"—two pairs of hooks for each bond. Note that the carbon still has its four bonds and the oxygen two. In ethylene we see a double bond between two carbon atoms. The long molecule is octanol, in which single bonds form a chain of eight carbon atoms.

For many molecules, ordinary chemical formulas, such as CO_2 for carbon dioxide (one carbon and two oxygens), or H_2O for water, or CH_4 for methane, will be all we need. But C_2H_6O could stand for dimethyl ether or for ethyl alcohol, two quite different substances, as you will see by studying their structural formulas in Figure 10-1. The alcohol is the substance that gives life to beer and whiskey, while the ether is a pungent, irritating gas. To know which substance we are discussing, it is necessary to know not only what atoms make up the molecule, but also how they are put together. That is why we represent these molecules by structural formulas. All kinds of combinations are possible, but only within the limits set by the number of bonds ("hooks") on each atom. Carbon always has four. Many atoms are limited to one bond each, such as hydrogen, chlorine (Cl), fluorine (F), sodium (Na), and potassium (K). Sulfur (S) usually forms two bonds, but may also form four or six. Nitrogen (N) usually forms three, but sometimes will form five bonds, as does phosphorus (P). Oxygen invariably forms two bonds. Once these bonding abilities are known, the next steps can be taken in the deduction of structural formulas.

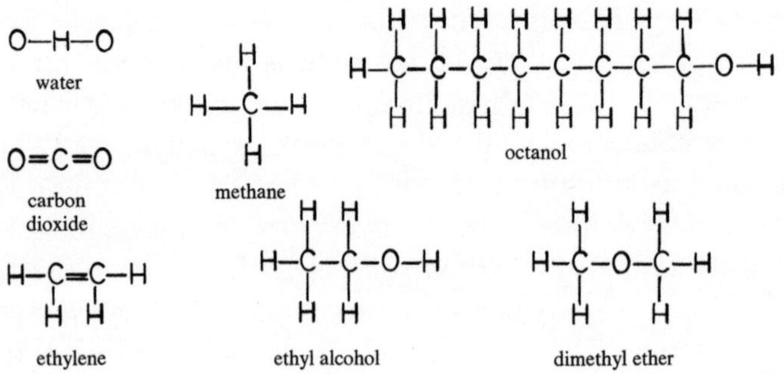

FIGURE 10-1. Structural formulas of several chemical compounds.

A chemical analysis of a mouse would reveal several thousand compounds at least, most of them organic. Let us list and classify these substances for future reference:

Water Water comprises about sixty-seven per cent of the body. Nearly every chemical process in the body, both within the cells and in the fluids between them, occurs between compounds dissolved in water.

Minerals These are inorganic materials, usually occurring dissolved in the cells and the body fluids. They occur as ions. The chief positively charged ions are sodium, potassium, magnesium, calcium and ammonium ($NH_4 +$). The chief negatively charged ions are chloride, iodide, phosphate ($PO_4 -$) and carbonate ($CO_3 -$). Some minerals also occur in solid form, such as the calcium phosphate of the bones.

Carbohydrates These are the sugars, starches, cellulose, and other materials. They are composed of carbon, hydrogen, and oxygen, with always twice as many atoms of hydrogen as oxygen. The simplest of them (the simple sugars) have the formula $C_6H_{12}O_6$, and these twenty-four atoms can be combined in many ways. Two molecules of simple sugar can combine by releasing a molecule of water to form a single molecule of double sugar ($C_{12}H_{22}O_{11}$). Figure 10-2 shows the structural changes that occur when a molecule each of glucose and fructose combine to form a molecule of sucrose, the substance in your sugar bowl.

The combining of sugar with sugar need not stop at a pair. Glucose is capable of *polymerization*; that is, one molecule after another can be added until thousands of them have joined together, eliminating a water molecule each time, to form a giant molecule. By the usual chemical nomenclature this should be called "polyglucose," but it occurs in several forms, the most common of which is starch. Polymerization is a crucial process in the chemistry of life,

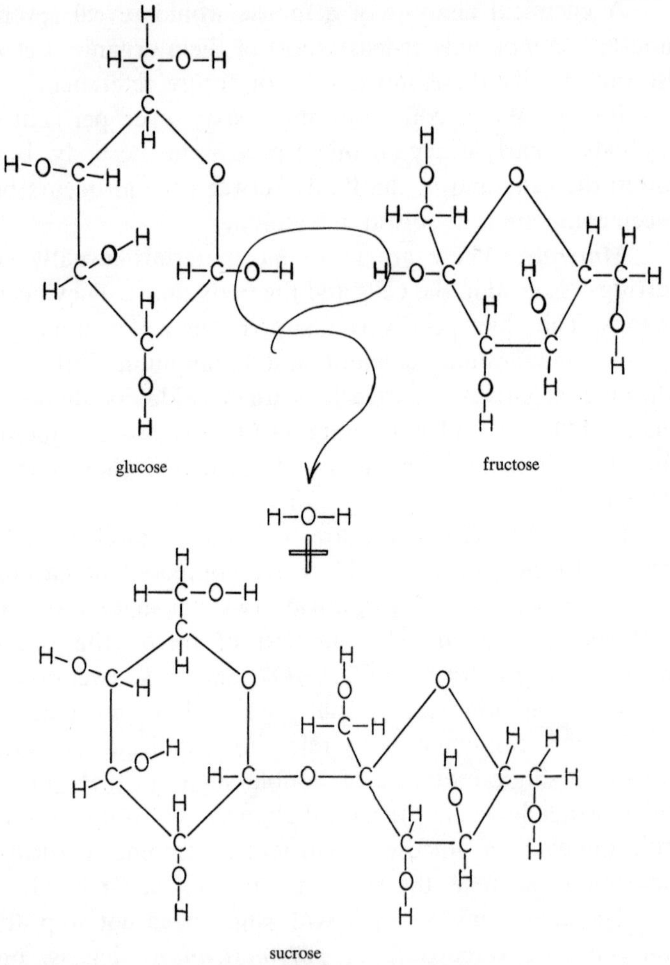

FIGURE 10-2. Glucose and fructose combine, with loss of a molecule of water, to form sucrose.

and man has lately learned how to control it for the production of such artificial polymers as buna rubber, polyethylene, polystyrene, and other plastics. Some of them consist of two kinds of molecules alternating in a long chain, such as the urea-formaldehyde resins used in hard plastics. Pectin, cellulose, glycogen, the starches, and others are polymerized carbohydrates.

Lipids These are the fats and oils. Figure 10-3 shows how a typical lipid is constructed, starting with glycerol and three fatty acids. Glycerol is always the base on which the lipid molecule is built. It possesses three carbon atoms, each of which has an OH group attached to it. At each of these groups, a fatty acid molecule can be attached by the elimination of water. The three fatty acid parts of a fat molecule may all be alike or they may be different.

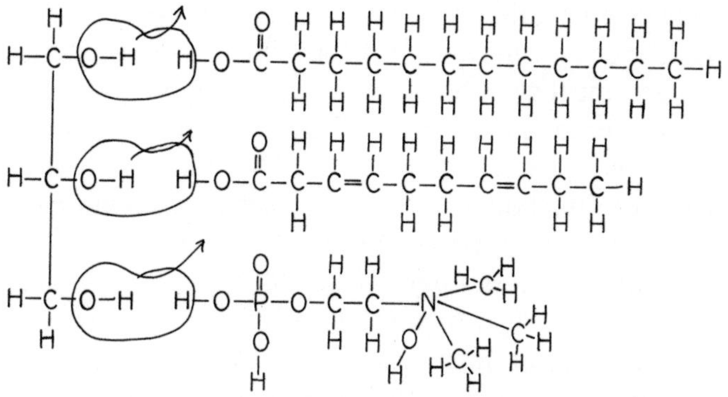

FIGURE 10-3. A glycerol molecule and three fatty-acid molecules combining to form a lipid molecule.

In the instance shown, one of them contains phosphorus, but more often all three are compounds of carbon, hydrogen, and just two oxygen atoms located at the end that fastens to the glycerol. A "saturated" fatty acid has two hydrogen atoms on every carbon atom, while an "unsaturated" fatty acid has two or more carbon atoms with only one hydrogen each, the carbons being attached by double bonds. Solid, animal fats are saturated, while the oils of vegetables and fishes are usually unsaturated. Figure 10-3 shows a saturated fatty acid, an unsaturated fatty acid, and a phosphorus-containing acid combining with glycerol to form a lipid. Note that the combination occurs in the same way as with sugars, by the elimination of a water molecule.

The lipids are high-energy material and constitute a concentrated form of stored food. You make a lot of them when you eat too much, and they are found where food storage is an important function, as in seeds and eggs. They are also important as structural material, since they are found in all cell membranes.

Steroids Steroids comprise a wide variety of organic chemicals containing much carbon and hydrogen but little oxygen and some nitrogen. Like the lipids, they are insoluble in water, but they contain neither glycerol nor fatty acids. The structure contains several rings of carbon atoms, like those of cholesterol (Figure 10-4). They have many special functions in the body and are best known as sex hormones, adrenal hormones, and vitamin D.

Alcohols, ethers, esters, ketones, aldehydes, etc. There are hundreds of other organic chemicals, mostly small molecules, making up intermediate products, chemicals with special functions, waste materials, and assorted molecules of no known function.

THE GIANT POLYMERS

Proteins In 1958, a group of chemists completed ten years of work and proudly presented the results: the complete structural formula of a protein. They had selected insulin, a small but most important protein, containing only 777 atoms of carbon, hydrogen, oxygen, nitrogen, and sulfur. Hemoglobin, an average-sized protein molecule, contains 9512 atoms, and a really large one may have several

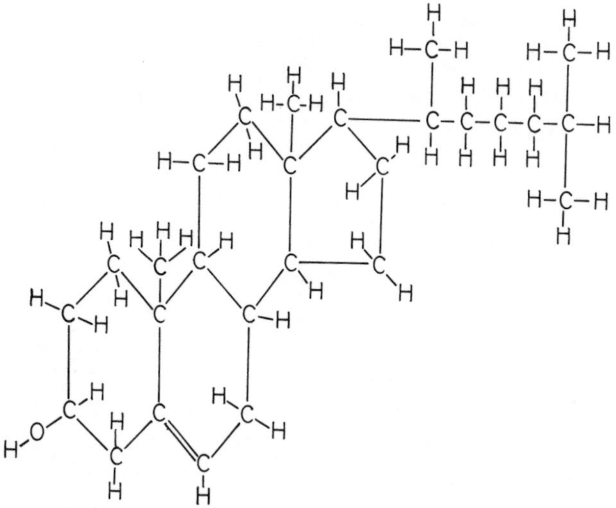

FIGURE 10-4. Cholesterol, a steroid.

hundred thousand. With proteins, we enter the world of complex, giant-sized polymers, different in a crucial respect from the giant carbohydrate molecules. Whereas a giant starch molecule (although not all of the complex carbohydrates) is essentially simple, because it is a monotonous repetition of glucose molecules, a protein molecule is a unique combination of a number of different, smaller molecules, each in its proper place in the larger structure. The starch molecule is like a brick wall made of identical elements and much like any brick wall, while the protein molecule is like a wall of fieldstone. Each part must fit into the whole in an individual way, and the result is unlike any other wall.

The protein molecule can be broken up into its constituent parts by chemical treatment, and the result is a mixture of twenty or so different organic chemicals of the

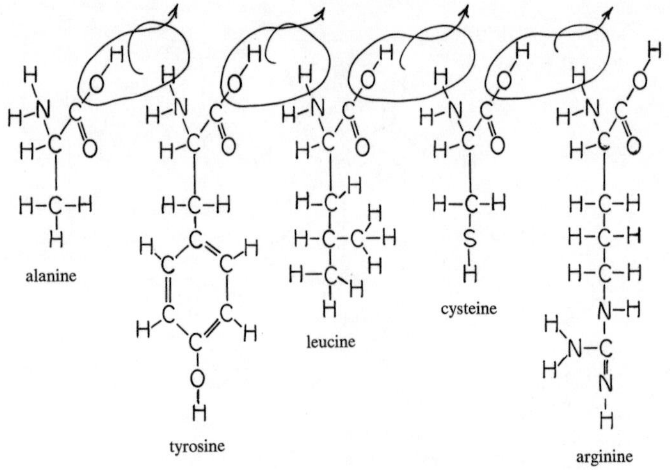

FIGURE 10-5. Several amino acids, showing how peptide bonds are formed.

kind known as *amino acids,* often with nothing else at all. Figure 10-5 shows the structural formulas of several of these amino acids. Note that all have a common structure at one end: two carbon atoms and a nitrogen atom in a row. The nitrogen atom bears two hydrogens (making the *amine* group) and the carbon atom at the other end bears two oxygens and a hydrogen (the *carboxyl* group which makes it an acid). The central carbon atom is connected to a group of atoms that distinguishes one amino acid from the others, the *side chain.* These amino acids can join together into giant structures because the amine group of any one can join the carboxyl group of another by eliminating a water molecule, as shown in Figure 10-5. Since the side chains are composed of carbon, hydrogen, oxygen, and sometimes nitrogen or sulfur, only five elements are needed to make the giant protein molecule. Many proteins are *con-*

jugated, that is, combined with organic chemicals other than amino acids, and these will often contain other elements.

Some fifteen per cent of an animal body is protein, more than all other organic compounds combined. These amazing chemicals do a variety of jobs in the body. The hemoglobin of the blood carries oxygen from lungs to cells. Tough fibers give flexibility and strength to skin, membranes, and tendons. Antibodies in the blood destroy invading bacteria, making us immune to diseases. Fibers in the muscles contract to make the parts of the body move. Gelatinous gristle lends shape and firmness to the ears, nose, and other cartilaginous parts of the body. Within the cells, the cell membranes and the ground material of the cytoplasm give form to cells. Hormones from the pituitary gland control the functioning of all the other glands of the body. One of the most important functions of proteins is to serve as enzymes, controlling every step in the countless chemical processes that are going on ceaselessly in the cells and the regions between cells.

How many different protein molecules can be made of the twenty natural amino acids? How many words could you make of a twenty-letter alphabet, assuming that you can make the words up to several thousand letters long? Clearly there is no limit. If you want a more precise picture of the degree of complexity available to proteins, you must write your words on cellulose tape and then crumple each strip into a ball, wind it into a spiral, or form any of a number of other structures with it. Even if you were to write identical words, how many ways would you have of giving the word-molecule a distinctive form? No one knows how many thousands of distinct proteins are found in the human body; many hundreds have been separated out and identified. The exact number and kind of amino acids—and often certain other molecules—making up many of these are known, but only in the case of insulin and two or three others is the order of amino acid units within the molecule completely understood.

Chemists have as yet been unable to synthesize any protein of average size. The largest protein-like substance yet made artificially is insulin, whose synthesis was announced in October 1963. It hardly ranks as a protein, for it contains only fifty-one amino acid units.

The complexity of protein chemistry extends even beyond this point. If a piece of skin is grafted from one part of your body to another, the grafted piece will grow in such a way as to unite itself with the adjoining tissue and will become a functioning part of your body. However, if a graft is made from one individual to another, the graft will be rejected; that is, the body of the person receiving the graft will produce antibodies that destroy the graft. Now what makes one piece of skin different from another? Its proteins! It is quite unlikely that there have been, in the whole history of our species, any two individuals with exactly the same combination of proteins. The only exception to this rule occurs in the case of identical twins, where one twin can donate skin or other tissue to the other. This exception throws an important light on the question of the source of these different proteins, as we shall see later.

Nucleic acids   In the past few years, these giant polymers have been found to have an overwhelming importance in the whole interlocking group of chemical reactions that we call "life." It is the special properties of the nucleic acids that result in molecular self-reproduction and the creation of specific proteins. These two processes constitute creation of life, the synthesis of living substance out of nonliving. The heart of all reproduction is to be found in the chemical interactions of the nucleic acids.

There are two general categories of nucleic acids: DNA

and RNA. DNA is found in the chromosomes of the nucleus, and RNA is found in both nucleus and cytoplasm. Any nucleic acid molecule is a giant polymer of different units called *nucleotides*. Figure 10-6 shows the structural formulas of the four usual nucleotides that make up an RNA molecule. Note that the nucleotide molecule is in three parts. At one end is a phosphoric acid group. The center is occupied by a five-carbon sugar called *ribose*, which gives its name to this category of nucleic acids (the ribonucleic acids, RNA). At the other end of the nucleotide molecule occurs one of four different *bases*, two of which consist of single rings and the other two of double rings. DNA (deoxyribonucleic acid) is similar, but in its nucleotides the ribose

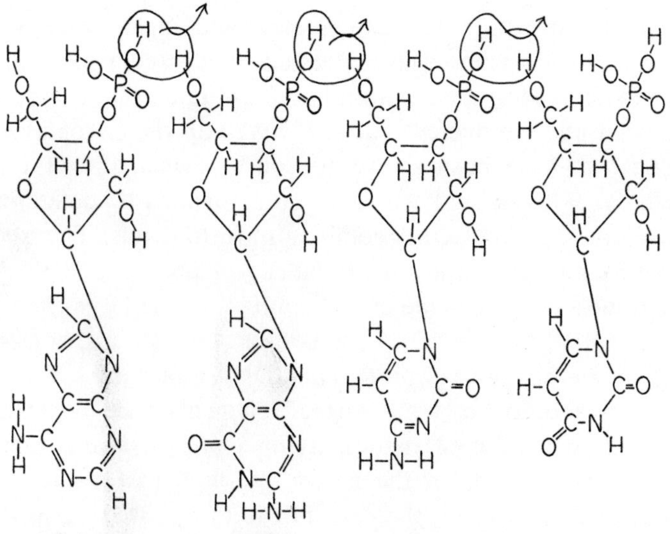

| | adenine | guanine | cytosine | uracil |

FIGURE 10-6. The four nucleotides that make up RNA, showing how they link.

sugar possesses one less oxygen atom, and one of the four bases is replaced by a different one.

The bases of RNA are called *adenine* and *guanine* (the double-ring bases) and *uracil* and *cytosine* (the single-ring bases). In DNA, the uracil is replaced by a different single-ring base, *thymine*. Later we will take up in detail the way these nucleotides combine to form nucleic acid polymers and how these giant molecules exert their biological control function.

CHEMISTRY OF CELLS

The boundary line between chemistry and biology has become increasingly vague in recent years and has all but disappeared wherever studies of cell structure are going on. The electron microscope has revealed the eleven-strand structure of cilia and centrosomes, and highly ingenious work by biochemists has suggested how protein molecules combine to form the strands. The membranes that surround the cell and the nucleus and that make up the endoplasmic reticulum have been shown to consist principally of proteins and lipids, and work is going forward to determine just how these molecules combine to form sheets. The ribosomes and nucleoli are made chiefly of protein and RNA. Chromosomes are made of nucleoproteins, the largest molecules found in cells. They are conjugated proteins, consisting of combinations of protein and DNA molecules.

In addition to these formed elements and the extracellular structures of tissues, living matter contains many fluids. The plasma of the blood, the fluid that bathes the cells, the fluid within the cells in the cytoplasm and in the nucleus, all have been subject to chemical analysis. Each fluid has its distinctive characteristics, but all consist mainly of water, with various mineral matter, simple organic chemicals such as sugars and amino acids, and also many proteins dissolved in the water. The chemical processes of living things take place in these fluids, either between dissolved materials or between the fluids and the formed structures, along the surface.

Hydrogen peroxide is an unstable chemical that spontaneously breaks down into water and oxygen. The process may be slowed up, taking years, if it is kept in brown bottles in a cool place. If hydrogen peroxide is put into contact with living human tissue, as it often is when used as an antiseptic, it bubbles violently, releasing in a few seconds the oxygen that might otherwise remain bound for years. The reason for this enormous acceleration of the decay of hydrogen peroxide is to be found in the presence, in human tissue, of a special protein called *peroxidase*. In some way this substance acts on the hydrogen peroxide to speed up its decay, but it will not have this effect on any other material. This illustrates the general properties of enzymes: they are proteins found in living matter, they greatly speed up chemical processes, they act specifically on certain processes only.

Nearly every chemical reaction that occurs in living things is controlled by a specific enzyme. Perhaps the best known enzymes are those responsible for digestion, the chemical breakdown of food that occurs in the stomach and intestines. You cannot make direct use of the giant protein molecules in your food. In your small intestine an enzyme splits off the amino acid units from the amine end of the chain, another splits them off from the carboxyl end, and a third splits the protein molecule at various points in the chain. Among them, they reduce the proteins in your food into amino acids that can enter your blood and be distributed through the body, serving as raw materials out of which you can create your own unique proteins. Other digestive enzymes similarly prepare carbohydrates and lipids. Within the cells are other enzymes responsible for preparation of food materials: to remove amine groups from amino acids in order to convert them into carbohydrates; to change one amino acid to another; to convert one form of sugar to another; to produce your characteristic lipids; to convert sugar into polymers for storage, and so on.

The investigations into the use of sugar by cells give us a fine example of the merging of biochemistry with cell-structure studies. The mitochondria of the cell have been known since 1903. They were found as a result of new staining techniques, for these tiny rods in the cytoplasm are not seen when the usual stains are used. At about the same time, an entirely different problem was being attacked which eventually shed light on the function of mitochondria. This was the investigation of the chemical processes by which sugar delivered to the cells by the blood is used to obtain energy.

It was known, of course, that sugar is oxidized, releasing carbon dioxide and water as waste products. This chemical reaction releases energy, just as the oxidation of oil can heat a house or drive an engine. In a long series of experiments, over a period of about forty years, it was found that the oxidation of sugar is a stepwise process. First the sugar molecule is combined with phosphate from the cytoplasm, then it is rearranged and combined with more phosphate, then split in half, then rearranged again, and so on, until only carbon dioxide and water are left. At several points in this process, the nucleotide called adenosine diphosphate, which is present in the cytoplasm, enters into the reaction and emerges with an extra phosphate group as adenosine triphosphate (ATP).

This extra phosphate group is a storage point for energy. The ATP formed in the oxidation of sugar moves to all parts of the cell, wherever energy is needed. Whenever a muscle contracts, a nerve conducts an impulse, a gland produces a special chemical, or a protein is synthesized, the energy for the process is supplied by removing the energy-rich phosphate group from an ATP molecule and reconverting it to ADP.

Nearly every step in the oxidation of sugar is controlled by a special enzyme that does one job and no other. There are over thirty such enzymes, and because many are available in pure form, these reactions can be recreated, carefully controlled, in a test tube. The enzymes of the last stages of the oxidative process are now known to be found in the mitochondria of the cell. The mitochondria can be extracted by whirling broken cells around in a centrifuge, and even in isolation they are capable of producing oxidation of sugar. The electron microscope has revealed that mitochondria consist of an outer wall enclosing a series of transverse plates. Each of these plates is a sheet of lipid material coated with proteins on both sides. It is now believed that the proteins on the surfaces of these plates include the enzymes that control the final steps in the oxidation of sugar and the transferral of its energy to ATP. Enzyme molecules are probably arranged in some kind of regular order, so that the various steps in the chemical breakdown of sugar occur in correct sequence. Our knowledge of the structure of mitochondria is now approaching the ultimate point, the understanding of the way individual molecules are arranged to account for both the structure and the function. Biochemistry is merging with cytology.

All biochemical processes involve enzymes. If your blood clots when you cut yourself, it is because an enzyme is released that acts to change a soluble blood protein into solid form. If your hair, eyes, or skin are brown, it is because certain enzymes are present in the appropriate cells which convert an amino acid into a pigment. It is probable that specific enzymes are necessary for production of the hormones that circulate through the blood and control your growth, development, and chemical activity. Even mental processes are completely dependent on enzymes; a certain form of feeble-mindedness, for example, is caused by a disturbance of the metabolism of an amino acid, due to the deficiency of a particular enzyme.

The complex processes of embryonic development undoubtedly owe part of their success to enzymes that control the chemical processes responsible for embryonic induction. The functioning of your enzymes and other proteins makes you live, gives you your human characteristics, and makes you unique among all the people of the world. If we are to understand what makes your body function as it does, we must study the proteins and try to understand how these proteins are produced, each with its own particular structure to give it the properties it needs to participate in the integrated activity of the whole body.

11

Reproduction at the Molecule Level

A living cell is a mass of feverish, complex chemical activity. Large food molecules are being reduced to workable size by digestion; excess food materials are converted from one form to another for new uses or for storage; sugars and fats are oxidized to provide the energy that all other processes consume so avidly; useless and harmful materials are changed into inactive form in preparation for their excretion; and in the midst of it all, the cell still finds the means and the talent to grow, to copy its own structure.

All these processes are so interconnected that disruption of any one will affect a great many others, perhaps leading to the death of the cell. The rates of all processes are controlled by the kinds of materials present; thus, if rapid growth is going on, amino acids are being consumed. According to well-known laws of chemical reaction, the shortage of amino acids speeds up those processes that produce amino acids. The result will be more rapid protein digestion (if any is going on at all), conversion of sugars to amino acids, or changes from one kind of amino acid to another, so that the balance of types will be maintained. Nearly all these processes are controlled by those astonishing proteins, the enzymes. Many of the proteins in any cell, both those dissolved in the cytoplasm and those making up the formed structures, act as enzymes. Most processes that we ordinarily think of as constituting life are functions of the special properties of proteins. Therefore, if we are seeking the origin of living substance, the crucial question to attack is the mechanism by which the cell manufactures proteins. We must also account for the specificity of action of the protein-synthesis mechanism. Why do pancreas cells make trypsin; bone marrow cells, hemoglobin; skin cells, collagen; and all cells, respiratory enzymes?

THE SYNTHESIS OF PROTEINS

As long ago as 1939, it was noted that cells actively engaged in the synthesis of proteins—cells of liver and pancreas, actively reproducing cells, the cells that produce the fibers of a silkworm cocoon—are always rich in RNA. It seemed likely that RNA is involved in the manufacture of protein, but this could not be tested until some technique was found to separate the RNA from the rest of the cell. This was finally done by the same technique that separated out the mitochondria.

Cells are crushed and placed in a centrifuge to be whirled around at enormous speeds. This causes the heaviest components to settle on the bottom of the centrifuge tube, and the others to form layers above in order of decreasing density. This technique makes available large quantities of fairly pure mitochondria, chromosomes, and other parts. When the ribosome fraction was analyzed, it was found to be about half protein and half RNA. In fact, most of the

RNA of the cell is found in these submicroscopic particles.

Once they were isolated from the cell, it became possible to test the role of RNA in protein synthesis. Ribosomes were added to a mixture of amino acids, energy-supplying chemicals, and certain enzymes, and the result was the formation of protein, identical to that formed in the cell from which the ribosomes were taken. Furthermore, addition of an enzyme that destroys RNA puts an immediate end to protein synthesis. It is an unavoidable conclusion that RNA in the ribosomes is involved in the synthesis of the specific proteins of a cell.

Obviously, any understanding of the mechanism of protein synthesis must depend on how well we know the RNA molecule. Somehow this molecule can take up amino acids from the cytoplasm and unite them together in a precisely determined order to make a specific protein. We know that the RNA molecule consists of a chain of four kinds of links, the nucleotides. Figure 10-6 shows how these nucleotides can link together by elimination of water at each junction. This can form a long molecule made of alternating sugar and phosphate units, with one of the four bases connected to each of the sugar units. All RNA molecules have this structure, and they differ from each other only in the number and arrangement of base units. As yet, no natural RNA molecule has been completely analyzed in the detail necessary to yield the complete picture of the molecule, but it is possible to make artificial RNA molecules with certain prearranged base-orders.

There is a form of RNA, found dissolved in the cytoplasm, which is called "transfer RNA," for reasons which will be made clear later. This material has been purified and studied by a technique known as X-ray diffraction. A beam of X-rays is sent against crystals of the material under study, and analysis of the directions in which the beam is reflected from the crystals makes it possible to learn a great deal about the spatial arrangements of the parts of the molecule. Transfer RNA's are small molecules compared with other giant polymers, only about eighty nucleotide units long. The X-ray diffraction technique shows that the molecule is folded in half like a hairpin, but with the two halves twisted around each other.

If transfer RNA is dissociated into its separate nucleotides, a peculiar and most important relationship is found. The number of adenine units is nearly the same as the number of uracil units, and the number of guanine units matches the number of cytosines. This clearly implies that the bases in the molecule exist in matched pairs. This and other evidence has led to the idea that the two halves of the molecule are cross-linked to each other, so that the A in one strand is always connected to the U in the other, and the G to the C. They are joined not by "hooks," but by a much

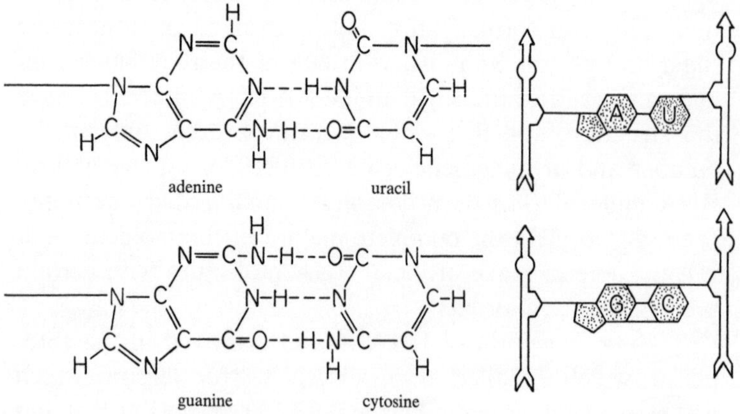

FIGURE 11-1. Pairing of bases of nucleotides. (*Left:*) chemical formulas (bases only). (*Right:*) outline of the whole nucleotide molecule.

weaker glue called a *hydrogen bond*. In this kind of bond, the hydrogen of an N-H combination can form a weak link either to another N or to a double-bonded O. If you study the four bases as shown, you will see that, with this limitation, the only possible way the bases can join together is A to U and G to C. It is these links that join together two parallel RNA strands as shown in Figure 11-1. Also shown is a method of representing this relationship that will make it unnecessary for us to write the whole structural formula each time we want to discuss this kind of molecule. The half-hexagonal knob represents the sugar and the circle the phosphate of the nucleotide. Figure 11-2 shows a short

FIGURE 11-2. Section of an RNA molecule. Code is
ACACGUUC.

section of this double-stranded RNA molecule. Note that the two spiral strands are kept a constant distance apart, because each rung of the twisted ladder consists of a one-ring base and a two-ring base.

The formation of A-U and C-G pairs is a crucial process, which we shall meet again and again as we delve into the molecular interactions that lead to self-reproduction of living matter. In fact, base-pairing is at the heart of many of the cell-building processes. The deviation from the 1:1 ratios in transfer RNA are presumed to be due to about three unpaired bases at the bend of the molecule, and several others at the ends.

Hundreds of the most ingenious experiments have enabled biochemists to piece together the mechanism by which cells make proteins. Most of these experiments are done in cell-free extracts, prepared by crushing living cells so as to destroy their physical structure and leave many chemical systems intact. To this, the experimenter adds the raw materials he is investigating, the nucleic acids and enzymes that bring about changes, and chemicals carrying the energy needed for the process. He may manipulate the experiment by controlling the temperature, the acidity, or the time allowed for the process. He then painstakingly extracts and analyzes minute quantities of the products of the reaction, and if he is lucky, he has found another piece of an endless jigsaw puzzle.

Much of the jigsaw puzzle is still missing, but the broad outlines of the picture have begun to emerge. In Figure 11-3, the process of protein synthesis is outlined, as it is now conceived to occur. It is based on many experiments, but it must be thought of as a tentative working model rather than a finished picture.

At the top, amino acid molecules (hook at one end, eye at the other, and distinctive group in the middle) are

Amino acid molecules unite with energy-rich ATP

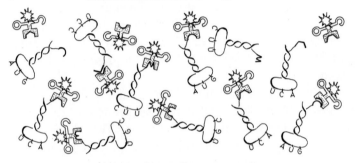

Activated amino acids combine with transfer RNA

Protein chain is formed in the ribosome

FIGURE 11-3. The synthesis of proteins.

shown combining with ATP (star). This is accomplished with the help of special enzymes and supplies the energy needed for the rest of the process. Each of the twenty amino acids needs a different enzyme for this process, which seems to go on all the time in the cytoplasm. Then (second drawing) the activated amino acid molecules combine with transfer RNA. There are at least twenty different kinds of transfer RNA. Each can fasten to a particular kind of amino acid by means of the unpaired bases at one end, and has a three-letter base code at the bend. Thus, when a particular protein is needed, all twenty activated amino acids, each combined with its specific transfer RNA, will be present in the cytoplasm.

When the cell requires a particular protein, a large molecule of the kind called "messenger RNA" leaves the nucleus and passes into the cytoplasm. The ribosomes are permanent structures, but they cannot function until they receive their short-term instructions from the nucleus. A ribosome fastens to one end of the messenger RNA molecule. The function of the ribosome is to select, from the mass of dissolved material moving through the cytoplasm, a particular kind of transfer RNA molecule which has just those three unpaired bases that will form A-U and G-C pairs with the first three bases of the messenger RNA. Since each kind of transfer RNA is joined to a specific amino acid, this has the effect of selecting a single amino acid molecule and putting it in place near the end of the messenger RNA molecule.

The ribosome now moves down the messenger RNA molecule (left to right in the third drawing), lining up the transfer RNA molecules according to the instructions coded in the messenger RNA. As the ribosome moves down, the amino acids, using the energy of the ATP, join together. This builds a chain of amino acids—a protein molecule.

The specific order of amino acids has been determined by the order of the bases on the messenger RNA molecule. The transfer RNA molecules, having served their function of translating the base-order code of the messenger RNA into an amino acid code, are released for further duty.

A messenger RNA molecule is much longer than a ribosome, and when proteins are being synthesized there will be a number of ribosomes lined up on the RNA molecule. They are spaced more or less evenly, and the number of ribosomes depends on the length of the messenger RNA molecule; there may be only four or five (when rabbit hemoglobin is being made) or over fifty (on the RNA of the poliomyelitis virus). The ribosomes start at one end of the RNA molecule and move along it to the other end, adding amino acids to the chain as they go. Thus a single RNA molecule serves as a template for the building of many protein molecules at the same time. The whole trip is completed in a matter of minutes.

THE BIOLOGICAL CODE

The kind of protein formed depends on which amino acids are aligned in what sequence, which in turn depends on the sequence of bases in the messenger RNA molecule, since each kind of amino acid has its own specific kind of transfer RNA to carry it to the ribosome. The messenger RNA carries a biological code, written in terms of the sequence of bases along the axis of the molecule.

Several important experiments have indicated that the code is probably universal; that is, that it is the same for all organisms. This was shown by adding RNA from tobacco mosaic virus, which normally lives only in the cells of tobacco leaves, to colon bacillus extract. The proteins made were almost identical to those of the tobacco mosaic virus, in spite of the fact that a colon bacillus normally makes nothing like it. Not content with understanding the mechanism of this process, biochemists are making great progress toward deciphering this code! The word "code" is chosen advisedly, for the research papers in this field are beginning to read more like Poe's "The Gold Bug" than like reports of biochemical research.

As any cryptanalyst knows, one cannot decipher a strange code without some knowledge of how the code is constructed. It is not possible that a single nucleotide specifies a single amino acid, for there are at least twenty amino acids and only four different nucleotides. Therefore, it is necessary to use more than one nucleotide to specify a single amino acid. It is something like using the four symbols of the Morse code (dot, dash, short space, long space) to symbolize the letters of the alphabet. Groups of two nucleotides each are still not sufficient, for there are only sixteen possible combinations. The minimum number of nucleotides that can specify all the amino acids uniquely is three, for there are sixty-four possible combinations (permutations, to be more precise) of four things taken three at a time.

Experiments have been devised to test the idea that every group of three nucleotides specifies a particular amino acid, and ample justification has been found. The idea that messenger RNA contains a triplet code for the amino acids is now widely accepted. With its acceptance it became possible to attack the code itself. Synthetic RNA made entirely of uracil units was added to a cell-free extract, along with all twenty amino acids. The only protein formed consisted entirely of the amino acid called phenylalanine. This implies that the RNA code for phenylalanine is UUU. Presumably, that species of transfer RNA with three unpaired A's at the bend can unite only with phenylalanine at the other end. The pairing of the AAA of the transfer RNA with the UUU of the messenger RNA would bring phenylalanine into position for joining the protein molecule. Other synthetic messenger RNA's were prepared and used in this way, and the nucleotide triplets for all twenty amino acids have been worked out.

This technique yields ambiguous results, for it cannot tell us anything about the *order* in which the three symbols appear in the code. Thus the code for both glutamic acid and aspartic acid consists of a U, an A, and a G, but in different arrangement. One important regularity did emerge, however, which made the next step in breaking the code somewhat simpler than it would otherwise have been. Every triplet contains at least one U. Of the sixty-four possible combinations, thirty-seven meet this condition. Synthetic RNA made entirely of U, except for a single A unit at the end, produced proteins of phenylalanine, as expected, but with a tyrosine unit at one end. This gave the correct order for tyrosine: UUA. Similarly, UUG turned out to produce cysteine. Once these two were known, all the others could be worked out from information already available in the literature of biological research.

The necessary information came from work that had been done with the process of *mutation*. It has been known for many years that a gene sometimes undergoes a change, producing an abnormal protein. For over thirty mutations, mostly in the genes of tobacco mosaic virus plus the one that produces hemoglobin in rabbits, it had been determined that the protein had been altered in a single amino acid, and this had been correlated with the change in a single nucleotide of the RNA chain. Thus it was known, for example, that changing a single U to a G will produce glycine instead of cysteine. Since cysteine was known to be coded UUG, glycine must be either GUG or UGG. Since UGG was known to produce no results at all, glycine must be GUG. By this kind of procedure, repeated for all mutations known in this detail, the specific order of the code for all the amino acids has been deduced. This breaking of the code must be considered tentative, however, for it must be confirmed in other organisms before we are reasonably sure that we can read the biological code.

The work with rabbit hemoglobin found twenty-five different combinations of nucleotides, in groups of three, that could specify an amino acid, and all twenty-five triplets contained U in either the first or the second place. There are sixty-four possible combinations, and they have all been tested by another technique. Synthetic nucleic acids were prepared using various combinations of nucleotides, and these were added to cell-free extracts. The resulting proteins were then analyzed.

With this technique, it is not possible to determine the order of the nucleotides in the code triplet, but there is no doubt that many combinations will work that do not contain U. There are duplications in the code; sometimes more than one code triplet will produce the same amino acid, and there is no evidence that any triplet is "nonsense"; that is, that it does not specify an amino acid. We would like to find evidence for a non-U triplet that actually works in a living creature under normal conditions.* We would like to know whether there is any "punctuation" in the code; that is, regions of the RNA molecule whose function is to separate one final protein molecule from the next.

The mystery of the self-perpetuation of living substance has been with us since man learned to think. The growth of scientific biology in the years up to 1950 gave us much insight into the nature of this process, but left the ultimate details behind a seemingly impenetrable wall. With new weapons, the electron microscope, the nuclear-age technique of labeling chemicals with radioactive atoms, with biochem-

* Both non-U and nonsense triplets have now been found in nature.

istry uniting with structural biology, the wall has been breached. The vista beyond is most exciting and will offer rich rewards to those who will devote their lives to its exploration. No man knows what lies in the distance.

FINALLY, THE GENE

Genetics, the science of heredity, became an exact science with the coming of the twentieth century. In the first decade, it became clear that the chromosomes, given to the zygote equally by egg and sperm nuclei, somehow served to control the development of the organism. Similarities between parents and children exist because the specific properties of the chromosomes remain unchanged by all the mitoses that produce the cells of the parents, the reduction division that makes the gametes, fertilization of the egg, and the subsequent mitoses in the offspring.

The early studies of heredity showed clearly that the chromosomes contained invisible particles, which are called "genes." Each gene has certain effects in producing observable physical and chemical features of the organism. No one ever saw a gene, no one knew what it was, but the experimental results obtained from crossbreeding led inescapably to the conclusion that they exist. Furthermore, they must be assumed to be self-producing, for the process of mitosis endowed each of the daughter cells with the same complement of genes. The genes are integral parts of the chromosomes, arranged along the chromosome in precise order and duplicating themselves when the chromosomes do.

The work of the biochemist has led to an understanding of what these genes are and how they work. Soon after biochemical genetics became a field of study in the 1930's, a pattern emerged of close correlation between the genes of the chromosomes and the proteins of the rest of the body. The disease known as sickle-cell anemia, revealed by crossbreeding analysis as due to a defective gene, was shown to be characterized in the first instance by an error in the structure of the hemoglobin molecule, a replacement of a single amino acid of this giant protein by a different one. Phenylketonuria, which is a form of hereditary feeble-mindedness associated with a disturbance of the body chemistry, was shown to be based on a failure of the body to produce a certain enzyme.

The problem of the relationship between the genes and the proteins was attacked in a systematic way in studies of the red bread mold *Neurospora*. Genes were altered by X-ray treatment, and it was found that each such change resulted in a deficiency of a particular enzyme. Today, hundreds of cases are known in a variety of species in which the effects produced by alteration of a single gene result from alteration of a single protein, and it is now abundantly clear that the primary function of the genes is to control the production of proteins. On this view, a "gene for brown eyes" is a gene that, in the appropriate cellular environment, generates an enzyme necessary for the formation of brown pigment.

Recent studies have gone far toward explaining how this process works. As we have seen, the proteins are made in the ribosomes, but their nature is controlled by the messenger RNA that comes to the ribosomes from the nucleus. It now seems clear that the function of the genes is to write the genetic code on the RNA molecules by controlling the synthesis of RNA with its nucleotides in a rigidly determined order.

A gene has another crucial function: it must duplicate itself in each cell generation. In other words, it must prepare a true copy of the code before each cell division.

The earliest hints of the chemical nature of the genes came from careful chemical analysis of cells. Extraction of

DNA from crushed tissue yielded quantities always proportional to the number of cells analyzed; in other words, the amount of DNA per cell for any given species is constant, regardless of what kind of tissue is used. This correlates well with the theory that DNA is the genetic material, for cell and heredity studies had indicated that the genetic complement of all cells in a given species is identical.

Now we look for the exceptions that prove the rule, and find that in haploid tissue (sperms), the DNA per cell is half as much as in diploid tissue. Again, just before cell division, the amount of DNA doubles. Special staining techniques showed that the DNA of a cell is localized on the chromosomes. When it became possible to obtain quantities of isolated chromosomes by the centrifuge method, chemical analysis showed them to consist of various proportions of protein and DNA. Biochemists began to suspect that the elusive gene, already known to be a part of a chromosome, consisted of a single molecule of nucleo-protein, a DNA molecule combined with protein.

The first clear-cut evidence that the genetic material is indeed DNA was the result of work with bacteria. Many variations are possible within a single species of bacteria in such properties as resistance to antibiotics, virility, susceptibility to attack by viruses, presence of external coats, form and shape of the colonies formed on culture media, ability to grow on different media, etc. The properties are maintained consistently through many cell divisions; that is, they are hereditary.

It is often possible to alter the characteristics of bacteria by treating them with purified DNA from another strain. The new feature will be a characteristic of the strain from which the DNA was extracted. Delicate statistical analysis has shown that a single molecule of a foreign DNA will be sufficient to alter a bacterium, and the new feature will be transmitted indefinitely to future generations. A gene has been added to the bacterial cell, and has become part of the genetic constitution of the organism.

Similar experiments have been tried on higher organisms, and one success has recently been reported. Human tissues suffering from a hereditary inability to make a certain enzyme were grown in tissue culture; that is, raised in vitro on a special nutritive medium. Treatment with DNA extracted from normal tissue caused the defective tissue to make the missing enzyme, and to keep on making it through many cell generations.

The long-standing mystery of what a gene is has apparently been solved, and we next would like to know how it works. From the work on protein synthesis, it would appear that the primary function of the genes is to make coded RNA. And it does. A cell-free extract is prepared, and the triphosphates of all four ribose nucleotides are added. If DNA is added to this mixture, the nucleotides will combine into an RNA molecule. Furthermore, it can be shown that the code in the DNA has been given to the RNA molecule. DNA contains no uracil, but has instead a different nucleotide, thymine. Its other three bases are the same A, C, and G as in RNA.

If DNA composed only of T is used in the experiment, the RNA formed is entirely A. If a mixed DNA is used, the fractions of A, C, G, and T in the DNA are the same, respectively, as the fractions of U, G, C, and A in the RNA formed. This probably means that the code is transmitted to the RNA molecule by the base-pairing mechanism. The same pairs are formed as in RNA pairing, except that the U of the RNA is replaced by T in the DNA. As yet, little is known about this process, although there is evidence that the pairing occurs successively from one end of the DNA molecule to the other.

Once the messenger RNA is formed in the chromosomes, how does it get to the ribosomes? No details are known for certain, although there are significant indications. Tiny droplets formed by blistering of the nuclear membrane adjacent to a chromosome have been seen to carry material out of the nucleus and into the cytoplasm. Possibly the canals of the endoplasmic reticulum carry these droplets to the ribosomes in their positions bordering these canals. The nucleoli are extraordinarily rich in RNA, but no one knows how it gets in or out. Possibly it stays there until the nucleoli degenerate in the early stages of mitosis, discharging into the cytoplasm the code for proteins necessary in mitosis.

One important point has been settled: the fact that the messenger RNA is short-lived indicates that the chromosomes do not simply instruct the ribosomes and then retire, but that the chromosomes exert a continuous control over the functioning of the cell. A chromosome is an engineer who supervises the day-to-day operation of the protein-factory, not one who designs the machinery and then lets it run itself.

These studies may sooner or later clear up another long-standing mystery, the mechanism of cell differentiation. No doubt our on-site engineer is continuously designing changes in the operation of the factory, in response to the demands of the rest of the organism. The chromosomes in some non-dividing cells are long, thin strands covered from end to end with tiny loops of DNA. There may be several thousand of these loops, and it is possible that they represent the genes. In some cells, it can be seen that a number of these loops are blown up into a tiny *puff* which is an active site of RNA synthesis. The number and location of these puffs depends on the kind of tissue and its stage of development. In the early embryonic stages, transplantation of a nucleus from one cell to another will produce a visible change in the chromosomes. New puffs will grow and existing ones will degenerate. These changes do not occur as readily in older tissue.

All these facts agree with the hypothesis that differentiation of cells is the result of differences in the activity of the genes, and that the activity of the various genes is somehow controlled by the environment of the cell. In one series of experiments, it was found that certain hormones can cause puffs to grow at specific locations on the chromosomes. One may speculate that inducing agents operate by encouraging or inhibiting specific genes in the competent cells, causing these cells to grow in one way rather than another by making the appropriate proteins. There is now some evidence that the protein part of the chromosomes plays a key part in responding to stimuli from the cytoplasm and controlling the activity of the genes.

MOLECULAR REPRODUCTION

If the DNA molecules are indeed the elusive genes, they must be capable of self-duplication. They are. If we repeat the experiments that showed how DNA synthesizes RNA, but supply the triphosphates of the four deoxyribose nucleotides instead of the ribose nucleotides, a tiny amount of DNA added to the mixture will result in synthesis of large amounts of DNA, identical with that originally supplied. This is molecular reproduction in a test tube. The mechanism of this reproduction has been investigated, and to no one's surprise is found to depend on base-pairing.

A DNA molecule consists of two long DNA strands, twisted around each other and cross-linked by base pairs. A single strand may have any arrangement of the four bases, but this then uniquely determines the order in the other strand. The pairs are always G-C and A-T (not A-U as in

RNA). Thus if a section of a single strand read GCGTTA-GCTTGA, the corresponding section of the other strand could only be CGCAATCGAACT, as shown in Figure 11-4a.

Pretty good guesses are available as to how this molecule duplicates itself. It probably occurs somewhat as shown in Figure 11-4. First, the hydrogen bonds linking the two strands break at one end of the chain. Each nucleotide of the chain then joins on to its mating nucleotide triphosphate, taken from the cell fluid. The high-energy phosphate

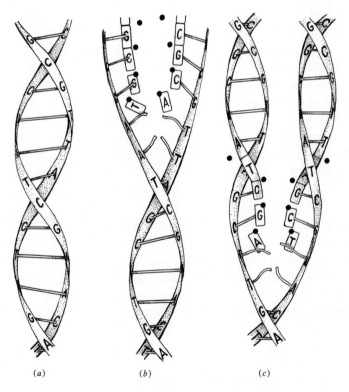

(a)   (b)   (c)

FIGURE 11-4. Self-duplication of the DNA molecule.

groups (black spots) then break away, giving up their energy to form the sugar-phosphate bonds that unite the nucleotides into a chain. In this way, each strand recreates the other, and there will be two identical DNA molecules where there was only one before.

Genes have another property that must be accounted for, their mutability. A most elementary knowledge of genetics must include the fact that genes occasionally undergo a spontaneous change. A female from a long purebred line of white mice will suddenly produce a black offspring, and the geneticist concludes that a gene in one of her eggs has undergone mutation, has changed in such a way that it produces a different physical feature. A large part of all mutations are lethal; that is, the change they produce is so drastic that the young die before they can develop into adults.

On the basis of our present understanding, how can we account for a mutation, for example, that produces a headless guinea pig? The headlessness would be due to the failure of some inducing agent to act at the appropriate moment in the embryology of the guinea pig. This is the result of some abnormality in the metabolism of the cells that normally provide the induction. This might be the result of the absence of some vital enzyme in these cells. Perhaps a single amino acid unit in the enzyme molecule has been replaced by a different one, thus changing the activity of the enzyme. The error in the amino acid would result from an error in a single nucleotide unit of the messenger RNA, which in turn would be caused by an error in a single nucleotide of the DNA in a chromosome. The mutation may have been an error in the duplication of the DNA code when the egg was formed, so that, let us say, an A was put in where a G should have been. Exact copying then puts the error in every cell, and the result is a headless guinea pig.

The nucleic acid molecule seems to represent the irreducible minimum of life. In appropriate surroundings, it can act as a template to duplicate itself, and it can cause changes in the chemical activity of its surroundings that will promote its own growth. The simplest living things, the viruses, consist of nucleic acid molecules that have these functions and no other. Virus particles outside of cells consist of DNA (or sometimes RNA) surrounded by a protein coat. When this particle comes into contact with an appropriate cell, the nucleic acid unit enters the cell, leaving the protein coat behind. In this hospitable environment, the DNA molecule commandeers the materials and the growth mechanism of the host cell and makes a copy of itself, repeating the process several times until several dozen virus DNA molecules are produced.

While this is going on, the electron microscope reveals no change, but then, quite dramatically, a new process starts. The virus uses the materials of the host cell to produce its own variety of messenger RNA, which travels to the cell ribosomes. The ribosomes therefore start to make proteins that the virus needs, instead of those required by the cell. This results in the formation of a new protein coat around each virus particle, so that in a short time all the virus particles appear. Within a half-hour of the invasion, the metabolism of the cell has been so completely disrupted that the cell dies and liberates the viruses, ready to attack another cell.

Is a virus alive? Obviously it cannot survive except in an environment where the normal cell machinery already exists. It needs the nucleotides, amino acids, enzymes, energy sources, and even the ribosomes of a living cell in order to complete its own life cycle. It seems unlikely that these particles could ever have had an independent existence, even in the organic soup that gave rise to life in the first place.

Many biologists feel that viruses are *free genes,* chromosomal DNA particles that have somehow gone bad and taken up a parasitic existence. This is supported by the fact that certain bacterial viruses are known to attach themselves to the genes of a host cell and to reproduce themselves in synchronism with the normal bacterial genes, thus behaving like a normal cell component! They produce changes in the cell metabolism, just as any gene might. Did they start out as genes in the first place and somehow become disconnected from the others?

It is remarkable how many of the most fundamental processes in living things depend on the base-pairing mechanism of nucleic acids. We study biology by many methods, investigating by different experimental techniques such phenomena as heredity, reproductive methods, regeneration of tissue, infectious disease, differentiation of cells, secretion of enzymes, formation of blood, even the evolution of living forms. As we pursue our studies from higher levels of organization to lower levels, we perceive underlying unities whose existence was unsuspected before. Evolution becomes the genetics of populations at the social level, physiological genetics at the individual level, cell differentiation at the cellular level, and eventually biochemistry.

All studies become biochemistry at the lowest level, and the nucleic acids lie at the root of the biochemistry of the cell. The law of life is increase, and the increase depends on the chemical process called base-pairing. This seems to foreshadow, in a way, the sexual processes that occur at higher levels, to be itself a kind of inchoate sexual process. This may not be mere analogy, for sexual reproduction cannot occur at any level unless preceded by reduction division, which can take place only if chromosomes form pairs. The pairing of chromosomes is a very precise, gene-by-gene process. Although nothing is known of how it works, it is possible that base-pairing could account for it. We have seen sexual reproduction at the organism level and the cellular level; we have seen a sexlike chromosome pairing at the subnuclear level. And now we find that a pairing process underlies all growth, all reproduction, everything that can be called life. It is tempting to conclude that sex is as ubiquitous as life itself.

Knowledge is power, power to control the forces of nature. As our understanding of biochemical processes broadens and deepens, as we learn to manipulate with ever-increasing delicacy and accuracy the processes of life, our power over the life of the earth, man's hegemony of the world, must inevitably reach new heights. No man knows where it leads.

Index